R A PARCEL

WAITING IN FOR A PARCEL used to be such a dull experience. The doorbe[ll] arranged, convenient time and a smart delivery man wearing a shirt & tie an[d] hand you your package. *Yawn! Yawn!* These days the process is much more [a] transaction with a delivery company inevitably becomes a nerve-testing battle [of wits taking days or] even weeks. It's everyone's favourite way to use up their holiday entitlement, but now you don't have to be expecting a parcel to enjoy that adrenaline-fuelled rollercoaster ride of incompetence, rage, broken promises, lies, dashed hope and suicidal despair. With our fantastic free **WAITING IN FOR A FUCKING PARCEL** game, every day is delivery day!

[...] on the mat inviting you to phone [...]ements to collect your parcel in [...] you do, even though it involves [...]ndswept industrial estate in the [...]ver your card at the counter you [...]th-breather wearing an ill-fitting [...]e is having trouble finding your [...] like. You are making progress.

5

After waiting another hour, you ring the bell to find out if there has been any progress finding your parcel. In response, twenty minutes later another mouth-breather emerges from the warehouse. You explain that his colleague is looking for your package, and enquire if he is making any progress. The new mouth-breather goes off to look, returning half an hour later to ask what the first mouth-breather looks like. This is more progress. **MOVE ON 2 SPACES.**

You wait for another hour, until the first mouth-breather returns through the warehouse door, still holding your card. He explains that he has been unable to find your package, and the chances are it is out on the van. You return home to find another card explaining that the driver called while you were out. **GO BACK 2 SPACES.**

After drinking eight cups of tea whilst waiting for your delivery, you can finally put off going for a piss no longer. You leave the toilet door open so you can listen out for the driver, who rings the doorbell exactly one nano-second after you start to urinate. You squeeze your pelvic floor in order to make the wee come out as fast as possible, and manage to reach the front door less than thirty seconds later. **MISS A TURN** while you stand on your front doorstep with a wet patch the size of a dinner-plate on your trousers, watching the delivery van driving off round the corner.

12

9

URGENT

[...]ou are promised a delivery [...]efore noon, so you take the [...]orning off. Unsurprisingly, the [...]an fails to turn up, and at twelve [...]'clock you give up waiting and [...]o to work. Returning home at [...]ea-time you find a card on the [...]at cheerily stating that the [...]river tried to deliver your parcel [...]t 5.25pm but you were out

Following a series of failed deliveries, increasingly irate phone calls and broken promises, the parcel company assure you that they will definitely deliver your package in the afternoon, so you will only use up half a day's holiday entitlement waiting in. Returning home at 11.55, you find a card on your mat stating that they tried to deliver your parcel at 8.37, five minutes after you left for work. **GO BACK TWO SPACES** while the vein in your forehead starts to throb.

You phone the delivery company to establish the whereabouts of a missing parcel. After waiting to be connected for more than an hour, you are eventually prompted to enter the 28-digit consignment number on your keypad. However, as you type in the final number, an automated voice tells you that your code has not been recognised and cuts you off. **MISS A TURN** whilst an ulcer begins to grow in your stomach wall.

24

Put off going for a slash. **HAVE AN EXTRA TURN.**

25

Put off going for a slash again. **HAVE AN EXTRA TURN.**

26

Amazingly, your parcel is delivered on time and to the right house. However, you open it to discover that the contents are smashed to fuck as it has been used as a ball for an impromptu five-a-side football match by bored drivers at the depot. **GO BACK TO THE START.**

After putting off having a slash all day, your bladder ruptures. Your body cavity is filling with a mixture of concentrated urine and blood, but you put off calling an ambulance in case you miss the driver. **GO BACK FIVE SPACES.**

URGENT

NEXT WEEK: Play *Pissing Away a Bank Holiday Monday Waiting in for a Fucking Skip*

THE BBC was plunged into a new storm of controversy last night following revelations about the filthy behaviour of some of its highest paid stars. Broadcasting House switchboards were jammed as an estimated 500,000 outraged viewers called to register their disgust at the filthy carryings on of such household names as JEREMY PAXMAN, FIONA BRUCE and TERRY WOGAN.

The outrage followed an expose in the *Mail on Sunday*, which detailed a catalogue of instances where highly paid celebrities had:

■ **URINATED** *in lavatory troughs during breaks in transmission.*
■ **BROKEN WIND** *in underground car parks at BBC Television Centre.*
■ **DEFECATED** *in BBC toilets within minutes of going on air.*

Singled out for particular criticism was £1million-a-year Newsnight host Jeremy Paxman who, according to the report, routinely passes lumps of foul-smelling excreta through his anus into various toilet bowls at Television Centre. An unnamed BBC source told the paper: "It's an open secret at the BBC that Paxman regularly locks himself in a cubicle in the gents, takes down his trousers and pants and spends ten minutes expelling germ-laden stools. He then wipes his backside with paper, washes his hands and comes back into the studio as if nothing has happened."

FILTHY

And the source said that the Cambridge-educated presenter was not the only Beeb high-earner to make a habit of such filthy behaviour.

"Terry Wogan is on £800,000 a year, but it doesn't stop him urinating in the gents at Broadcasting House up to six times a day," he added.

As part of his sordid routine, Wogan likes to unzip his flies and remove his penis from his trousers. The filthy Radio 2 breakfast host then points his organ towards a toilet trough in order to direct a stream of his urine. Not content with that, he then shakes his manhood to remove any remaining drips from his prepuce.

RICH

Wolverhampton housewife Edna Bile was typical of the many Wogan listeners who rang the BBC to register their disgust. She fumed: "I'm appalled that my licence money has gone to fund this disgusting man. I've listened to Radio 2 every morning for twenty years, and I never imagined Sir Terry getting up to that sort of filth. It turns my stomach."

Female stars at the corporation were also implicated in the scandal. Former newsreader Fiona Bruce came in for criticism after it was revealed that she had released noxious gases from her bowel on more than one occasion.

CATFLAP

"Bruce is the BBC's golden girl," the source said. "But she got the job on the Antiques Roadshow despite everyone knowing that she breaks wind from time to time. Admittedly she is professional enough to hold it in when she's on air, but as soon as the director shouts cut, anything goes."

"Millions of viewers may tune into her shows, but they would switch off in disgust if they got wind of her filthy flatus," he added.

MPs were quick to join in the condemnation of the corporation. "A culture of filth has been allowed to develop at the BBC," raged shadow culture secretary Sir Anthony Regents-Park. "The BBC used to be a byword for decency and standards. It seems to have gone down the toilet, quite literally. This once fine broadcaster is now submerged under a tide of urine and faeces."

Labour spokesman Lord Twatt agreed. Speaking from the yacht of a Russian oligarch vague acquaintance he said: "The BBC used to be something that the whole country could be proud of. But it has been allowed to become a cesspit mired in its own foetid effluent, a giant septic reservoir of reeking turds."

PISSFLAP

"There needs to be a root and branch cleansing, before the entire corporation is engulfed by a stinking tidal wave of ordure," he added.

BAN THIS FILTHY BBC FILTH

DIRTY BASTARD

Filthy Filth of the Filthy Rich Beeb Stars

DIRTY DEN: *BBC Broadcasting House yesterday.*

Fap! Fap! Fap! Fap! Fap! Frosh! It's

THE · FIVE · KNUCKLE · SHUFFLE

THE CREAM OF ISSUES 172 TO 181 BEATEN OUT UNDER STIFF COVERS

CHRISTMAS PUDS:
Graham Dury, Wayne Gamble, Stevie Glover, Davey Jones and Simon Thorp

CHRISTMAS STOCKINGS:
Alex Collier, Simon Ecob, John Fardell, Barney Farmer and Lee Healey, Robin Halstead, Jason Hazeley, Harry Herring, Christina Martin & James MacDougall, Alex Morris, Joel Morris, Graham Murdoch, Paul Palmer, Lew Stringer, Cat Sullivan & Nick Tolson

BOXING DAY LOG:
Russell Blackman

Dennis Publishing Ltd., 30 Cleveland Street, London W1T 4JD

ISBN 978-1-907232-91-6 | First Printing Autumn 2010

SUBSCRIBE ONLINE AT
www.viz.co.uk

Viz Comic, PO Box 656
North Shields NE30 4XX
e-mail: letters@viz.co.uk

CHEESE BILLIONAIRE STAR LETTER

■ 30 years ago, the Irish were our most feared terrorists and now they have theme pubs everywhere. So by 2047, will Britain be full of Islamic Extremist theme pubs? Because I don't much like the sound of that. **Nick Pettigrew, London**

As writer of this issue's Cheese Billionaire Star Letter, Mr Pettigrew wins a £billion of cheese, donated by our friends at www.iwantabillionpoundsworthofcheese.com

■ What a cheek Ann Widdecombe has got condemning prostitutes when she knows nothing about the lives they live. When she's worked the streets turning tricks for a couple of months, then and only then will she have earned the right to critiscise prostitutes. Mind you, if she did go on the streets, I for one would not pay to do her. Not unless she did unprotected anal, which I very much doubt she would. And even if she did, I wouldn't pay more than £30.

G Bulgaria, Lemmington Spa

■ The hypocrisy of Ann Widdecombe staggers me. She is not prepared to take money off men for unprotected anal sex, oh no! But she'll happily take money off food companies to advertise their pasta. Perhaps if the pasta company had offered her money to advertise anal sex, it would have been a different story. As usual, it's one rule for the pasta companies and another for the ordinary anal sex punter in the street.

H Marmaduke, Tewkesbury

■ I must admit, I'm not sure where I stand on the Ann Widdecombe hypocrisy debate. You see, on the one hand I'm obsessed with anal sex, but on the other hand, I'm not that fussed on pasta.

D Baddiel, London

■ Could I request that your readers please stop writing in about having anal sex with Ann Widdecombe, protected or otherwise. I'm trying to eat my tea.

H Mountjoy, Leeds

■ Regarding my recent letter about paying for unprotected anal with Ann Widdecombe. I have been having a bit of a think, and I reckon I would go up to £40.

G Bulgaria, Lemmington Spa

■ Kelly Brook vowed to remain on *Strictly Come Dancing* after the death of her father as it is what he would have wanted. Having a whole nation of men watching your daughter's tits jiggle about the place seems like an odd final wish to me.

Nick Pettigrew, London

■ To the ambulance driver filling in the *Daily Mirror* crossword puzzle whilst driving along the Coast Road in Newcastle yesterday afternoon. Three down was pigeon.

J Thorn, Hexham

■ I dont know what all the fuss is about these so called arranged marriages. Me and my wife spent 6 months arranging our marriage and it went fine.

Rob, Santa Pola

■ To the woman in the departure lounge at Newcastle airport. When the EasyJet representative asked for passengers with young children to board first, I don't think she had your son in mind, who must have been 15-years-old and at least as many stone.

Bjorn Polaxe, e-mail

■ People shouldn't be allowed to put quick drying glue onto road crossings. Someone could get stuck in mid stride and be run over by a lorry, or worse, a steam roller.

Ada Brassknobs, Carlisle

■ My wife and I recently had a wonderful holiday in Saudi Arabia. We took in all the local atmosphere of the street markets, the smells and sounds of the bazaars, and lost a little bit of money at a camel race. We even went to a public beheading. My wife was in two minds whether or not to attend, but I reminded her 'when in Rome, do as the Romans.'

Humphrey Plywood, Berkshire

■ I bought my young grandson a Lego AT-AT Star Wars vehicle this Christmas. But when he opened the box, I was horrified to see that it was smashed to pieces. He didn't seem to mind, but I certainly won't be buying from that company any more.

Hector Cretis, e-mail

■ The BBC showed themselves up to be foolish by censoring the word 'faggot' from the Pogues and Kirsty McColl Christmas song *A Fairytale of New York*. 'Faggot' is a perfectly good word for a savoury rissole, or a bundle of sticks used as fuel. And it is one of these, entirely inoffensive, senses in which I use the word when screaming it through my neighbour's letterbox, or scratching it on his so-called 'civil partner's' car door.

Ernest Britain, e-mail

■ 'You're never too old to learn,' so the saying goes. I don't know. My gran is 102 this year and I reckon it's a safe bet that she is never going to take up and master the bagpipes now.

Bartam Farnborough, e-mail

■ I recently found a picture of Paris Hilton fully clothed and with her nipples inside her top. That has to be worth something. I will except £5

Dawn Keebals, e-mail

■ I've smoked 40 cigarettes a day since I was 13, and I've never had a day's illness in my life. Tomorrow I celebrate my 80th birthday, and I'm going to stay in the house all day and watch telly so as I don't get ran over by a bus.

Albert Nobacon, Bedlington

■ I was driving on the A69 the other day when I saw a sign that said 'Stationery Vehicles Ahead'. I was just thinking which thicko spelt stationery with an 'e' when I ran into the back of a WH Smith lorry.

Brian Norman, Cumberland Infirmary

■ Surely Steve McLaren's biggest error was telling us to judge him on results. That's just asking for trouble. If I were England manager, I

FRED WEST BASSET

...ZZZ!

FRED! WAKE UP!

HAVE YOU BEEN BURYING THINGS IN THE GARDEN AGAIN?

Ooops! Caught red pawed..!

WAG Alex Curran. It will take Gerrard at least half an hour to earn back the money to pay for replacements. And in the meantime Alex will be forced to make do with the 2 rooms full of clothes and accessories she was boasting about in *Closer* magazine this week. Poor lamb.

Christina Martin, e-mail

think I'd tell the nation to judge me on punctuality, or my attendance record.

Cormac Purtill, e-mail

■ I matched three numbers on Saturday's Lottery. Do I win £10 ?

Martin Smith, e-mail

■ My grandad smoked 40 cigarettes a day from the age of 13 and never had a day's illness in his life. Yesterday, on his 80th birthday a bus skidded on a patch of ice and ploughed through his living room wall while he was watching the telly. He was killed instantly. And they say smoking is bad for you!

Kirsty Nobacon, Bedlington

■ Shame on those burglars for breaking into Stephen Gerrard's mansion and stealing some of the huge amounts of jewellery owned by pointless

■ My wife and I recently came back from a holiday in Afghanistan where we went to a football stadium to see the public stoning of an adulterous woman. My wife thought it was a little cruel, but I reminded her that this spectacle goes back hundreds of years, and we have to respect other peoples' cultures and traditions.

Humphrey Plywood, Berks

■ I'm a bus driver, and I have lost count of the number grandfathers I have run over and killed on their 80th birthdays after they have enjoyed a lifetime of illness-free heavy smoking. My nerves got so bad as a result of all the accidents that I took up smoking and immediately caught cancer. If only I had listened to the people who said smoking was bad for you.

Frank Bowles, e-mail

■ What a smashing idea for Christian businessmen to put the little fish symbol in their yellow pages adverts. It's good to know that I can call a plumber who will not only turn up two days late and charge double his quotation, but when he does turn up, he'll believe in fucking fairies.

Frank Fibreboard, Luton

letters@viz.co.uk

Calls for New Medical Standards

THE British Medical Association have released new guidelines for doctors, specifying a change in the fruits used to describe the size of tumours, cysts and other bodily growths.

OUT go tumours the size of old-fashioned gooseberries, apples and grapefruits and IN come trendy lychees, avocados and papayas.

According to BMJ Chairman Dr Robert Chartham, the new standards are being driven by the changing market for more exotic fruits. He told us: "Thanks to the likes of Jamie Oliver and Nigella Lawson, the public now demands a more sophisticated selection of fruits on its supermarket shelves. It's only right that the medical profession reflects this when describing the results of tests and scans."

"Using more up-to-date fruit comparisons is an effective means of vividly bringing patients' worst fears to life in the twenty-first century," he added.

The new doctors' guidelines, which are expected to cost over £10 billion to implement, are the most wide-ranging since the use of fruit was originally adopted, replacing sports balls of various sizes, in the early 1960s.

But pensioners' leader Dolly Earnshaw was quick to hit out at the changes. "My members have only just got to grips with the last set of changes," she fumed. "We were perfectly happy with our lumps being the size of cricket balls, thank-you very much. This latest change is even more confusing. Us old folk can't tell the difference between a starfruit and a plantain, let alone a mango and a Chinese lantern."

"It's just changing things for the sake of changing things. I don't like these fiddly new five pees neither. Everything was much better in the old days. They should send them all back," she added.

Despite the new fruit guidelines for tumours, the BMA says that traditional comparisons will remain unaltered in other areas of medicine. "There will be no change to the description of bumps on the head, which will continue to be compared to the sizes of various eggs," said Dr. Chartham.

Supermarket Hot Seat Strikes Again!

EXCLUSIVE!

25 members of staff at the Walsall branch of Sainsways Supermarket have all become PREGNANT in the past 12 months... *after sitting on the same manager's cock.*

Store boss Lennie Tripper told the Walsall Herald: "I don't know what it is about my cock. I've lost count of the number of employees who have fallen pregnant after sitting on it. It might be a coincidence, or it may have magical properties. All I know is, this mini baby boom is costing me a fortune in maternity pay."

But Tripper is finding that his lucky cock is causing some headaches at work. "Some of my staff whose families are already complete are refusing to sit on my cock in case they fall pregnant too," he said. "I think they're being a bit superstitious, but I can't force them to sit on it."

When the story was featured on the front page of the local paper, Tripper's magic cock became the talk of Walsall. "Now it's not just the staff," he told reporters. "I've even had requests from ladies trying to conceive, all asking me if they can have a sit on my lucky cock."

"Well, if it brings them a little hope, I'm only too happy to let them," he added.

~ Reuters

9

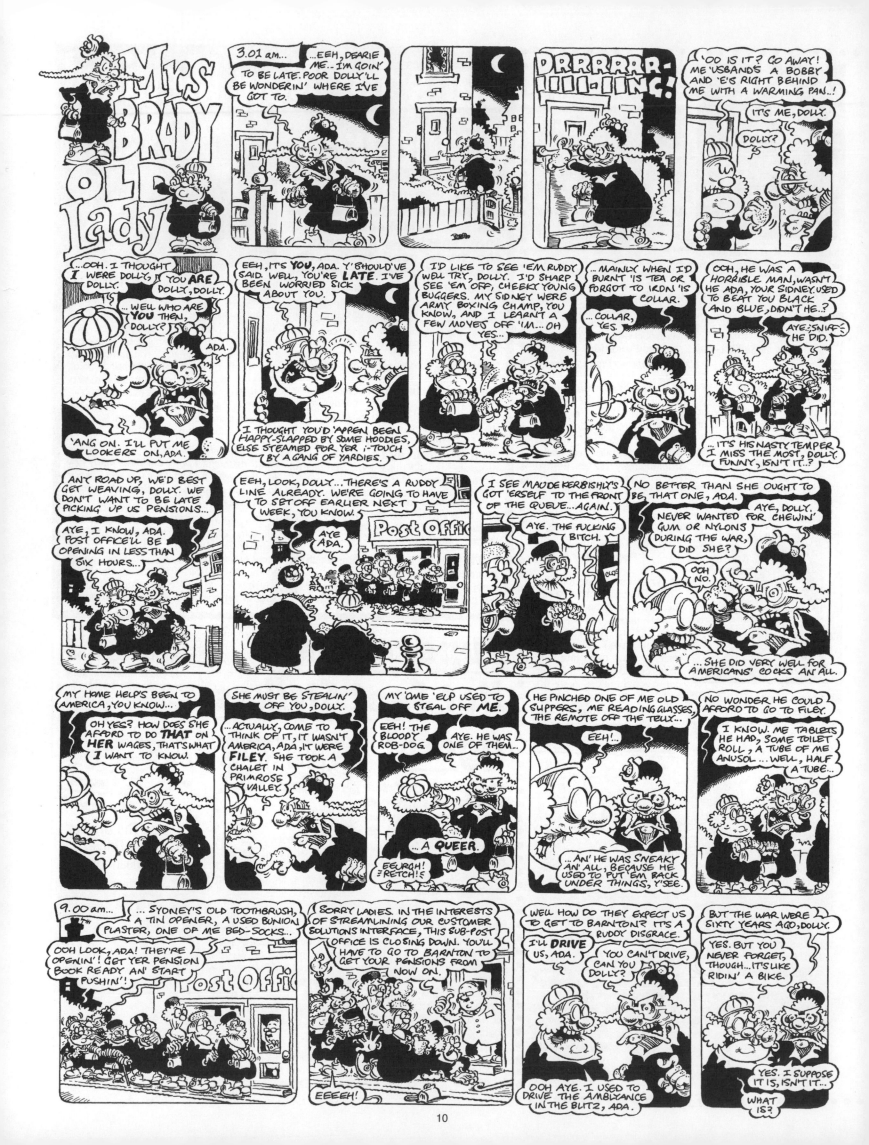

DRIVING, DOLLY.

OOH, YES. 'OLD ON THOUGH. YOU AVEN'T GOT A **CAR.**

WELL, WE CAN BUY ONE, ADA... I'VE BRANG ME TEAPOT WITH ALL ME SAVINGS IN... I NEVER LEAVE THE 'OUSE WITHOUT IT, I DON'T...

EEH!

I DON'T TRUST THAT 'OME 'ELP OF MINE, YOU KNOW, ADA.

YOU DO RIGHT, DOLLY.

GOOD MORNING, LADIES... ARE YOU LOOKING FOR ANYTHING IN PARTICULAR..?

A **CAR.** WE'VE GOT TO GET TO BARNTON TO COLLECT US PENSIONS.

..PENSIONS, YES.

HOW ABOUT THIS ONE... THE SATSUMA PISTACHIO GLX? IT'S GOT EVERYTHING... ABS...

ABS... YES...

...XENON HEADLAMPS...

...XENON. FANCY...

...IT'S FULLY EQUIPPED WITH NINE AIRBAG'S...

EEH! YOU DON'T WANT NINE AIRBAGS, DOLLY. YOU CAN'T SEE WHERE YOU'RE GOING WHEN YOU 'AVE A CRASH, OOH **NO.**

...THREE-POINT INERTIA REEL SEATBELTS, FRONT SEAT PRE-TENSIONERS...

...CATALYTIC CONVERTER, DRIVER'S AND FRONT PASSENGER'S SUN VISORS WITH COVERED AND ILLUMINATED COURTESY MIRRORS...

I LIKE THE COLOUR. IT'S THE SAME AS ME SISTER'S TOILET. I'LL 'AVE IT.

IT'S ALL THERE. I'VE COUNTED IT. AND DON'T YOU GO TRYING TO DIDDLE ME OUT OF ME CHANGE, YOU THIEVING TURK. I'M NOT SO GREEN AS I'M CABBAGE-LOOKING, YOU KNOW.

EEH! THESE SEATS ARE LOW, DOLLY.

RIGHT MADAM, IF YOU'D LIKE TO STEP INTO THE OFFICE, I'LL SORT OUT THE PAPERWORK FOR YOU.

EEH! THESE SEATS **ARE** LOW, AREN'T THEY, ADA..?

V-VROOM! VROOOM! VROOOM!

GRIND!

'ERE WE GO...

VROOOM! CRUNCH!

YOU'RE ALRIGHT MY SIDE, DOLLY.

IS THERE OWT COMIN', ADA? ONLY I'VE ONLY GOT ME LOOKERS ON... SHOULD'VE BRANG ME SEERS.

CAREFUL, DOLLY... LEFT HAND DOWN A BIT...

CRASH!

WINSOME WELS MOTOR DEALER

GRIND!

...D'YOU KNOW..? I DON'T THINK I **DID** DRIVE THE AMBLYANCE, COME TO THINK OF IT, ADA. THAT WAS ME BROTHER BILLY... I USED TO WORK IN THE CORDITE FACTORY.

8 HOURS LATER...

...I'M GETTIN' THE HANG OF THIS NOW. WE'LL BE THERE IN NO TIME!

WELL, AS LONG AS WE GET THERE BEFORE THAT RUDDY MAUDE KERBISHLY...

...SHE CAUGHT THE SICK, YOU KNOW... **VEE DEE.**

NEVER!

OH YES. OFF A B52 PILOT.

WELL, WHEN HER HUSBAND COME BACK FROM BEING SHELLED AT GALLIPOLI, HE WERE NONE TOO PLEASED, I CAN TELL YOU, ADA.

WELCOME TO BATTLEFIELD DOCKS

MIND, **HE'D** GOT ROOM TO TALK BECAUSE HE'D GOT IT HISSELF, IN VALETTA OFF A WREN FROM LEEDS.

EEH! THERE'S A PAIR OF 'EM.

...AYE. I KNOW.

YOUR SIDNEY COME BACK FROM NORTH AFRICA WITH VD, DIDN'T HE, ADA?

YES, BUT HE CAUGHT THAT OFF A TOILET SEAT, DOLLY...

...FROM THE LAVVY IN AN ALGERIAN BROTHEL.

½ AN HOUR LATER...

...I'M BEGINNING TO THINK WE'VE 'APPEN PASSED THE POST OFFICE, YOU KNOW. I DON'T RECOGNISE ANY OF THIS ROUND 'ERE, DOLLY...

...PULL UP 'ERE, LOVE. I'LL WIND ME WINDOW DOWN AND ASK THIS BOBBY FOR DIRECTIONS.

1 THE MOTOR workshop is traditionally a male-dominated environment, and as such can be a slightly intimidating place for a visiting female customer. To make women drivers feel more at home in the garage, these mechanics have thoughtfully put up a calendar featuring a picture of a pretty girl. This touch of femininity amidst a masculine environment is a good way to put lady customers at their ease.

People Who Help Us

The Garage Mechanic

MODERN CARS contain miles of wiring, and a simple electrical fault can be almost impossible to track down and remedy. Here, a customer has brought his car into the garage because the interior light in the boot has stopped coming on. The mechanic tells him he has located a short circuit in the car's expensive, state-of-the-art CD radio, which he has removed. This will later be recycled and sold on to another customer. The mechanic has also replaced the bulb in the boot light.

2 IN A traffic accident, it's often just the front or back of a car that is damaged beyond repair. Scrapping the whole car in these circumstances would be a waste of precious natural resources. Here, the ingenious motor engineer is welding together two such salvaged halves, in order to recycle their components into a perfectly good, brand new car which may give many months' service to an unsuspecting young family.

3 WHEN THEY fail, it can be uneconomic to replace certain large motor car components. This gearbox, for instance, is dangerously worn after many hundreds of thousands of miles of driving, but it would be prohibitively expensive to fit a new one. The canny mechanic decides that the best course of action is to "mend and make do", and fills it with sawdust. This simple, yet effective procedure, which makes the gearbox feel as good as new, will allow it to work smoothly once more, giving its owner up to several dozen miles of carefree motoring.

MANY CAR parts can be fitted to a number of different models made by the same manufacturer. Here, a customer has paid to have a brand new stainless steel exhaust pipe fitted to his family hatchback. However, the motor engineer fits the expensive new system to his own car, which is of the same make, and generously gives the customer his own, slightly used - yet still perfectly serviceable - exhaust at no extra charge.

A MODERN MOTOR CAR is a very complicated piece of machinery with thousands of moving parts. Gone are the days when, should it go wrong, we could tinker under the bonnet ourselves. Today we must take it to an expert - the Garage Mechanic. In many ways the garage mechanic is like a surgeon: he knows how to diagnose and cure the mechanical illnesses that affect our cars' systems. He has trained for many years to do his job and uses specialised tools to carry out complex procedures. And, like a surgeon, he also has the ability to take an arm and a leg off you.

Let's take a look behind the scenes at a typical motor engineer's garage.

WHEN any repair has been made, it is important that the motor mechanics test-drive the car to make sure it is functioning correctly and safely. This vehicle, which was brought in to have a new radiator fitted, has been thoroughly tested over the course of a weekend, being driven long distances at top speed over various terrains. Happily, it has passed with flying colours!

GARAGE MECHANICS like to belittle their customers by moving the driving seat as far back on its runners as is physically possible. This driver returns to pick up his vehicle and the mechanics gather to watch him pathetically having to slide his seat forwards until he can reach the pedals and steering wheel.

4 **THIS MOTOR** engineer is a perfectionist. He has decided that the brake pads on this woman's car, although practically brand new, need to be replaced. In order to avoid confusing the customer by showing her the actual pads from her car, he shows her a set of badly-worn brake pads from another vehicle.

5 **BY LAW,** contaminated fluids drained from vehicles must be collected by a registered disposal company. However, calling their lorry all the way out to the garage in order to collect a relatively small amount of used sump oil would create an unacceptable amount of pollution, causing global warming. So this environmentally-responsible mechanic does his bit to save the planet by tipping it down the drain.

6 **SOME INTERMITTENT** faults reported by customers don't show up during servicing. To find out the specific circumstances that led them to occur, this mechanic makes a phone call to a young woman who brought a car in which keeps losing power on hills. Like a detective, he has to know every detail of her driving style in order to diagnose the problem correctly and make the necessary repairs. He asks her whether she rests her hands on the gear lever whilst driving, whether she drives in high heel shoes and what colour knickers she is wearing.

7 **DURING THEIR** regular maintenance regime, many car owners fail to make routine checks on the spare tyre in their boot well. Here, the mechanic takes advantage of this fact by swapping this customer's brand new, spare alloy wheel for a barely-legal budget re-mould on a rusty steel rim. This good spare is fitted to another customer's car, making it safer on the road for everyone.

NEXT WEEK: People Who Help Us
The Estate Agent

IT had been a harsh winter in the Peebleshire hills. High on the fells above their cottage, Andrew Selkirk and Black Bag, his faithful border binliner, were watching the sheep frolicking in the crisp, white snow. "Ye ken, baggie," the shepherd chuckled. "It does ma heart braw guid tae see a' ma lambies haein' a few last hours o' fun afore they gan awa' tae their doom at the slaughterhoose in Auchtermuchty this aftaenoon."

SUDDENLY, Selkirk heard a terrified bleat. He and Black bag turned and watched in horror as a tiny lamb hurtled out of control on its tea-tray toboggan...straight over the edge of the crag! "Och no!" he cried. "It's Morag, ma favourite wee sheep. Yon cliff's over fufty oor saxty feet haigh. If the poor wee thing isnae dashed to fuck on the rocks below, she'll be drooned in the River Peeb as sure as haggis is haggis!"

SPLASH! The little lamb hit the freezing Highland water. Struggling for breath, she managed to scramble up onto a piece of floating ice. High on the crag, the shepherd sighed with relief. "Thank goodness Morag's safe, Baggie," he said. "A'll just pop doon tae the riverbank and lift her oot." The binliner fluttered in the wind in agreement, and the pair set off down the steep path towards the fast-flowing brook below.

HALFWAY down, Selkirk suddenly stopped and gasped. "Help ma boab!" he cried in horror. "A've forgotten to bring ma shepherd's crook! A must've left it in ma but'n'ben this mornin' afore I came oot. Wi'oot ma crook, I've nae chance of fishin' wee Morag to safety afore she goes o'er Peebles Falls!" There was no time to run home to fetch his crook. But Bag had had an idea, and started flapping excitedly in the breeze.

ANDREW spread Bag out on the snow and sat on him. They soon began to pick up speed. "Jings, yon's a michty fast way tae travel!" shouted Andrew as he sped down the slope on his faithful polyethylene pal. "But it's playing havoc wi' ma bloody piles! Och! Ma poor ringpiece!" It took Selkirk and Bag just seconds to get back to their cottage, where the absent-minded crofter had left his crook in the umbrella stand.

BLACK Bag knew there wasn't a second to lose before poor Morag was swept to her death over the raging waterfall. He blew excitedly along the riverside path as fast as the breeze would carry him, and his master wasn't far behind with his trusty shepherd's crook. "Don't worry, ma wee woolly lassie, Andrew's comin' tae save ye!" he shouted. "Mind, ma Cairngorms are gi'in' me an affy lot o' gyp after yon ride doon the glen on Bag!"

THE rescue party got to the waterfall just in time. Bag snagged himself on a tree so that Andrew could lean right out over the icy torrent to reach the precious lamb with his crook, just as the chunk of ice on which she was standing was swept over the falls. "Well done, lad. There wisnae a baw'hair in it," he smiled. "And as fair you, Morag, you're safe noo." The grateful little sheep licked the shepherd's face with relief.

LATER that afternoon, Mr McLecter arrived to pick up the sheep and drive them to his abattoir in Auchtermuchty. Black Bag lent a hand bringing them down from the fell and herding them up the ramp into the lorry. "Keep an eye on wee Morag here," said Andrew. "The poor lassie had a narrow escape this aftaenoon." "Dinnae worry, Mr Selkirk," chuckled Mr McLecter. "A'll mak sure she disnae escape frae ma bolt gun!"

Simon Cowell's EGGS FACTOR

eggs r gr8! i luv em ;-). eggy bill. Eggs are the @1 fd 4 me. yum yum yum. the eggman.

Lv the white. H8 the yoke. Help!. johnny albumen.

EGS R 4 SADOS. BACONS BEST. FUK EGS U EGFUKERS. BAMBER G

Get ur facts str8 bamber g. bacon suks. eggs 4 evr. egg warrior.

My six-year-old grandson has been doing sex education at school, and it's filled his young mind with all sorts of weird and wonderful ideas. The other day, he came round for tea and asked what we were having. When I replied that it was eggs, he piped up, "Are we having sperm on them?" As you can imagine, there was a ghastly, embarrassed silence, and a very unpleasant, awkward atmosphere for the rest of the evening.

Mrs Audrey Clutchfluid, Leominster

HI THERE EGG FANS! TV's Mr Nasty Simon Cowell, here. And as usual, you've been writing to me about eggs. And it's no 'yolk' to say that this week's Eggs Factor postbag is the biggest I've ever had! So without further ado, 'shell' we 'crack' on and 'dip' in?!

My husband had a boiled egg for his breakfast every day of his life, and he lived to the ripe old age of seventy-eight. It just goes to show that scientists don't know everything.

Mrs Yootha Turpentine, Hull

My wife and I both love eggs, but cooked in different ways. She likes hers scrambled, whilst I prefer mine poached. Sadly, the strain of our egg preparation preferences eventually proved too much and drove a wedge between us. We eventually got divorced the day before our Golden Wedding Anniversary. I am now remarried to a woman who likes poached eggs as much as I do, and I am happier than I have ever been.

Harold Meths, Leicester

These food fascists say that eating too many eggs is bad for us. Well for their information, I eat far too many eggs every day and there's nothing very serious wrong with me. Once again, the so-called "egg-sperts" are left with egg on their faces!

Jemima Diesel, Bicester

I was on holiday in America recently and a waitress in a restaurant asked me if I wanted my eggs "sunny side up". I had to laugh. She'd got it wrong and meant fried!

Mrs T Vaseline, Gloucester

I'm mad about eggs, and I was very excited to see a programme called *Eggheads* listed in the *Radio Times*. Imagine my disappointment when I tuned in to discover that it was a general knowledge quiz show. Fortunately, there was a question about eggs so my half hour wasn't completely wasted.

Frank Butanol, Pwllelli

My husband and I were playing Scrabble the other night. When it came to his turn, he drew two Gs, an S and an E, but announced that he was unable to make a word out of those letters. How foolish he felt when I pointed out that he could have made the word "eggs". The funny thing is, he's an egg farmer...and his name is Ronald Eggs!

Edna Eggs, Worcester

I was on holiday in America recently and a waitress in a restaurant asked me if I wanted my eggs "over easy". I had to laugh. She'd got it wrong and meant fried again!

Mrs T Vaseline, Gloucester

As a devout Catholic, my wife refuses to eat eggs because she says they are chickens' abortions. But I don't mind, because I'm an atheist and that means more eggs for me. I love 'em!

R Butane, Cambois

I'm a Muslim and I don't eat eggs, but it's nothing to do with my religion. They give me really smelly wind.

Iqbal Benzene, Tunbridge

When my son was little, I cooked him boiled eggs for breakfast every morning. Now he is an SAS swimming instructor, based in Exeter. He often jokes that he used to dip his soldiers in his *eggs*, whereas now he dips his soldiers in the *Exe* - the river which runs through Exeter. However, this isn't strictly accurate, as they have a swimming pool in the camp. And in any case, the soldiers get in of their own volition, thereby dipping themselves. And he never had bread & butter soldiers when he was little, as he is gluten intolerant. And he's not in the SAS either. He just tells people that to impress them.

Marjorie Hydrocarbon, Shrewsbury

I was on holiday in America recently and was leaving a restaurant after eating two platefuls of fried eggs. After I paid the bill the waitress told me to "have a nice day". I had to laugh. She'd got it wrong and meant goodbye!

Mrs T Vaseline, Gloucester

I'm sick of show-off TV chefs breaking eggs using just one hand. If the good Lord had meant us to break eggs like that He would have given us one hand, not two. It would serve these people right if they lost an arm in an accident like the drummer out of Def Leppard.

Archbishop Rowan Williams, Canterbury

Readers' Wives' Eggs

How about this pair of scrumptious frieds I snapped on my missus's plate! It will give her a real thrill to think of all your hungry Eggs Factor readers drooling over them.
Name & address withheld, Altrincham

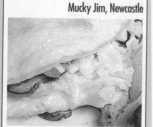

Check out this close-up omelette shot of my young wife's 2-egg breakfast. Believe you me, I scoff one of these down every day and it's as hot and delicious as it looks!
Mucky Jim, Newcastle

Send your Egg-splicit Photos to the usual address.

Miriam's Egg Problem PHOTO CASEBOOK

Jess's Frying pan Dilemma: *Day 6*

Jess has been going out with her boyfriend Tom for five years. But whilst frying him an egg she has accidentally dropped a bit of shell into the pan...

Oh No! There's a bit of shell in the pan.

Tom hates shell in his egg.

If I get it out with a fork I might burst the yolk...

And I can't use my fingers because it's a bit hot...

Jess confided in her mum...

Oh, mum. I'm so confused...

Should just keep quiet about it? He may not find it, and what he doesn't know won't hurt him.

No, Jess! If Tom finds that bit of shell in his egg, you'll have lost his trust for ever.

But what should I do?

I don't know, Jess. You'll have to get the shell out somehow, and quickly...

...because if you leave it on the heat much longer, that egg is going to be like *rubber!*

Oh no!

Continues next week!

Excuse Me Madam...

Are You Bei

TO MILLIONS of viewers, he will always be remembered as the camp Mr Humphries from 70s sitcom *Are You Being Served*. With his mincing walk, slack wrist and eagerness to measure a gentleman's inside leg, we all took it for granted that JOHN INMAN was as gay as the day was long.

But, according to a man claiming to be the actor's former window cleaner, nothing could be further from the truth. In real life, says Albert Vennison, Inman was 100% heterosexual and had a ravenous, insatiable appetite for sex with women. "Inman certainly led the British public a merry dance," he told us from the modest Clacton bedsit he shares with two of his brothers. "And from my unique vantage point up a ladder, looking through his windows, I saw the lot." And now, on the anniversary of his death in 2007, Albert has decided to lift the lid on the late actor's secret, straight life.

SEMI

"Like every other TV viewer, I had always assumed that Inman was on the other bus, but I found out how wide of the mark I was the first time I went round to clean the windows at his swish Croydon semi. I had gone up my ladder to do the back bedroom. Inman's house had double glazing units with a UPVC frame, and unlike other window cleaners, I prided myself on always cleaning the frames as well as the glass. But I must admit, I forgot about cleaning either when I peered through into his room. There, on Inman's bed, was a huge pile of naked women, all writhing and moaning in ecstasy. There must have been nine or ten of them, all without a stitch on. I am a red-blooded man, so I settled back to watch.

EXCLUSIVE!

"Suddenly, in the middle of the pile, trapped between a load of tits, appeared a familiar face. It was John Inman, and he was grinning from ear to ear! When he saw my boggle-eyed face looking in through the curtains, he gave me a cheeky wink. 'I'm not free!' he quipped, before giving each woman in turn a multiple orgasm. Twice. Not a lot of window cleaning got done that day, I can tell you. I was perched up that ladder watching the action for more than three hours before they all collapsed exhausted on the bed."

HARD

That was the first time that Albert saw the star's carefully cultivated gay mask slip, but it certainly wasn't to be the last.

HEAVY

"At first I assumed that what I had seen was just Inman experimenting, and that he was still one of them really. But how wrong I was, as I found out the very next day. In the window-cleaning business, it's always a mistake to think you can get away with using dirty water as it can lead to streaking and smearing on the glass. I had just filled my bucket with a fresh load from Inman's outside tap, and I happened to peer in through the kitchen window. At first, I had to pinch myself to make sure I wasn't dreaming. I couldn't believe my eyes.

"There must have been twenty women in there, all of them beauty queens, exotic dancers and busty page 3 models. They were all stark naked so you could

see everything, and they were fighting over Inman's manhood. Eventually Inman vanished into the pantry, returning seconds later with one of those ticket machines you get at the cheese counter in the supermarket. He made each of the ladies take a ticket and then bonked them in strict rotation, quipping his catchphrase 'Are you being served?' before taking every one them to the heights of sensual pleasure. And back.

"After he had finished with them, each woman went to the back of the queue and got another ticket! The only thing that brought the orgy to an end was when the machine ran out of tickets and the women had to get dressed and go home. There wasn't a lot of window cleaning got done that day either, I can tell you."

SCRAP

Vennison now knew of Inman's secret double life, and how his on-screen gay persona was at complete odds with his red-blooded private life. So it came as quite a shock when the next day he witnessed Inman being intimate with just ONE woman as opposed to a dozen or more.

BATTER BIT

"I had just washed the window of Inman's boxroom and was about to take the suds off the glass. There are a lot of charlatans in the window cleaning game, many of whom use an old car windscreen wiper for that job. I, on the other hand always insisted on a proper window cleaner's squeegee. They may cost a bit more, but they do a professional job. Anyway, as I started, I saw Inman on his spare bed in a naked clinch with a woman. I looked around for the others but was amazed to see that she was the only one. I thought that the *Are You Being Served* star was perhaps losing his touch, until I saw a familiar looking pointy bra hanging off the lampshade on the bedside table.

"The woman in Inman's arms was none other than Madonna, the most desired woman on earth. I watched incredulously, repeatedly squeegeeing the same bit of window over and over again, as Inman made love to her for fourteen straight hours. I lost count of the number of times she climaxed,

WHEN I'M CLEANING WINDOWS: You should of seen what I of seen, says Albert.

STRAIGHT UP: Was camp Mr Humphries a secret stud?

ng Serviced?

but it looked like he took the sex goddess to new heights of fulfilment, heights she could never have achieved with Guy Ritchie, Sean Penn, Warren Beatty or any of the other blokes who have banged her. If she was like a virgin when she went into Inman's bedroom, she certainly wasn't when she came out, I can tell you. In fact, she was walking like John Wayne by the time he'd finished with her."

TRUE

Cow-tongued Kiss frontman Gene Simmons claims to have slept with over 4000 women in his lifetime. This may or may not be true, but what is for certain, says Vennison, is that the Grace Brothers Casanova regularly beat Simmons's record... in a single day!

"Never trust a window cleaner who uses washing up liquid in his bucket. My reputation is build on a squeaky clean finish, the kind of finish that can only be achieved using special, professional window polish that is solely available to the trade. However, this day I ran out of the stuff whilst I was doing Inman's windows, so I decided to knock on his door to ask if I could borrow a bit of washing up liquid. However, when I got to the front of the house, I couldn't believe my eyes.

GOLD

"There was a queue of women stretching out of his door and all the way down the street! In amongst them, I thought I recognised some of the Nolan Sisters, a few of Pan's People, the girls out of Hot Gossip and Hill's Angels off the Benny Hill Show. Inside the house, the line continued up the stairs and right into Inman's bedroom, where the man himself was servicing them one by one, taking each in turn to shattering levels of erotic rapture. Outside the room, security guards were asking the women to strip off in readiness so that Inman could keep his rate of turnover up. Once he had finished with them, the sexually satiated women were helped down the

back stairs by staff, given a cup of tea and a biscuit before being ferried away in a fleet of double decker buses.

MARS

"He may have looked effeminate and feeble on screen, talking to Mrs Slocombe about her cat, but when it came to the ladies, Inman's sexual stamina could only be compared to that of a rutting stag. He was insatiable. Inman served more women that afternoon than he ever did at Grace Brothers. I counted 5000 in through his bedroom door and I counted 5000 out. And he took every single one of them to a hitherto unimagined peak of carnal delirium."

AZTEC

Sadly, says Vennison, that particular encounter was to be the last that he was to have with the *Are You Being Served* stickman. That evening, a slight misunderstanding in the grounds of his local nurses' home led to the 53-year-old bachelor losing his job and being put

on the sex offenders register. "It was a terrible pity, because I loved my work and the unique window it gave me onto the lives of my customers," he told us. "In the end I decided it would be best to up sticks and try my luck in another town under an assumed name. I moved to Nuneaton in Warwickshire and set up a new window-cleaning round. To my surprise, my first customer was *Generation Game* host Larry Grayson."

GAY

"But the first time I climbed up my ladder to clean his bedroom windows, I got the shock of my life. For the amazing scene that met my eyes was a million miles away from the gay personality Grayson projected on screen."

I'M FREE: Inman was always available for sex with ladies, says Vennison.

GRACE BROS

Star Letter

★ I WAS surprised to see the racist abuse of Lewis Hamilton by Spanish F1 fans at the Circuit de Catalunya in Barcelona. You wouldn't think the Spanish would be racist, what with them being foreign themselves.

Edna Golightly, Luton

I WONDER how Michael Foot's family are referred to by their neighbours. Do they say 'the Foots have gone away for the weekend' or do they refer to them as 'the Feet?'

Jamie McCredie, Newcastle

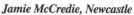

I WAS saddened to hear about the death of Abdul Latif. I went to his restaurant a few times and he was a really nice bloke. Nothing was too much trouble. As a mark of respect, how about printing that picture of a bloke kissing that bird's arse, but both wearing black armbands.

Big Jim, Manchester

* Good idea. Here you go, Big Jim.

I'M SURE I'm not the only person who has noticed the bizarre mismatch between the hair and eyebrow colour of our former Chancellor of the Exchequer Alistair Darling. And I'm sure I'm not the only one who is wondering what colour his pubes are. Do they match his hair or his eyebrows? They might be ginger for all we know. Until he comes clean about the hue of his short and curlies, how are we supposed to trust anything he says about the economy?

T Thorn, Hexham

* Are you a male MP? Have you ever stood next to the Chancellor of the Exchequer in the bogs at the House of Commons and seen his pubes? Write and tell us what colour they were. There's a crisp tenner in a plain brown envelope for any MP who spills the beans.

CELEBRITY SWEARS

No. 509 ~ The Bee Gees

Big bowl of dicks

Fat fucking tits

Tosser

MY husband died last month and I had him cremated. A friend suggested that as part of the mourning process, I should scatter his ashes in the place where we first met. I took comfort from this idea. We met at the salad bar of our local Pizza Hut, but when I started emptying his urn into the grated carrots, the manager came over and rudely asked me to stop. The insensitivity of some people is beyond belief.

Edna Waitrose, Luton

I AM 97 and I still have all my own teeth. I've kept them in a jar in my cupboard since I had them all removed in 1948.

P Grummet, Nottingham

IF GOD is all mighty and all knowing, you'd think that he'd know that pi is equal to 3.14159 etc. But in *1 Kings ch.7 v.23* in the Bible, it says that it equals 3. I hope the Archbishops of Canterbury's wheels fall off his fucking car.

B Lions, Nottingham

WITH reference to the above letter, I am a vicar and I agree with God that pi is equal to 3. That is why the earth is fatter round the equator than it is round the poles. If pi equalled 3.14159, it would be a perfect sphere, which it isn't.

P Withe, Nottingham

I AM a teacher at a leading faith-based city college, and the foundation of all our educational philosophy is that the Bible is the word of God and the truth. Consequently, in biology we teach creationism as explained in the book of Genesis, and in mathematics we teach that pi equals 3, as stated in the book of Kings. Anyone pupil who believes in dinosaurs, or who puts 3.14159 into equations for pi is taken into the playground and stoned to death against the boiler-house wall.

Mr Emmanuel College, Gateshead

I'VE just done a really big turd and it would be a shame to flush it away. Does anyone know Jim Davidson's address?

L Lloyd, Nottingham

PRINCE Edward, Prince William, Prince Charles - what is it with our royal family going bald at an early age? Goodness knows what they cost us enough in taxes each year. You'd think they'd manage to hold onto their hair for us past their twenties.

Crompton Filofax, Dudley

I AGREE with Mr Filofax *(above)*. The royal family are bone-idle parasites with nothing to do all day. They've got all the time in the world to keep their hair and they can't even be bothered to do that. I'm a self-employed electrician who works 16-hour days, and I have a head of hair like Brian May. What kind of example are these royals setting?

K De Mange, Leeds

I FEEL I must write and defend the royal family against these accusations that they are too idle to keep their hair. On the contrary, they work extremely hard. Prince Edward for instance, is a very busy television producer. He produced *It's a Royal Knockout* in 1987, and he's probably been so busy since, working on new TV projects that he hasn't had time to think about keeping his hair.

TS Ball, Leeds

THE BBC business correspondent defended Shell's massive £14 billion profit by pointing out that they help the British economy by paying a billion pounds in tax each year. That's 1/14th of their profit. I'm a plumber and I seem to end up paying a third. Does anybody know who Shell's accountants are?

D Doogan, Wolverhampton

I'M A transvestite and I was recently thrown out of Westminster Abbey because I was wearing a dress and a hat. But when the Archbishop of Canterbury turns up in a dress and a hat, they roll out the red carpet for him. Once again, it's one rule for bearded transvestites and another rule for the rest of us.

P Parkes, Wolves or QPR

'Lunar Pond Plan a Winner' says NASA

US SPACE AGENCY boffins say that craters on the Moon would make "smashing little fish ponds."

Professor Jackson Pallo, head of Lunar Colonisation Research told reporters: "A pond always brightens up a garden, and I'm sure it would do the same for the moon. Let's face it, it's not the most interesting of places, and a nice pond with a fountain would look wonderful. There is also the advantage that you wouldn't have to dig a hole, just fill a crater with water."

When we called pop star Sting, who had a hit with *Walking on the Moon*, he said: "I'm in the middle of fucking my wife at the minute. Ring me back in about four hours"

I CAN'T see what all the fuss is over this latest bugging row. Infringing someone's civil liberties by listening in to a conversation is a small price to pay for public safety and we should thank the security services rather than criticising them. In fact we must all do our bit and remain vigilant if we are to defeat the terrorist menace in our midst. I myself rent out a small bedsit to two student nurses, and I have installed surveillance equipment in the shower in case either of them goes in there to make a rucksack bomb.

H Granville, Luton

TOP TIPS

■ I'M NOT gay and I haven't got the best gaydar in the world, but could someone explain how, out of John Barrowman and Russell Brand, it turns out that Brand isn't the gay one.

Rob Ellis, Birmingham

■ I WISH Lady Diana, Queen of Hearts, was still alive. Not because I liked her, but because if she was, everybody would be sick and tired of her by now and I wouldn't have to hear about her half as much as I currently do.

Martin Cristoph, e-mail

■ I SAW a few weeks ago that a man had been arrested trying to smuggle 2 kilograms of cocaine into the USA. Then last week I heard a man got arrested trying to smuggle 10 kilograms of cocaine out of the USA. I wish they'd make their minds up, do they want the stuff or not?

Pete T, e-mail

■ I CONDUCTED a survey with a few of my friends the other night and it was unanimous; if any of us became an evil dictator, we would grow comedy facial hair. Is there a scientific explanation for this?

Jack Bumsworth, e-mail

■ IS RICKY Hatton his real name, or is it just a nickname because he's always got a hat on I wonder?

Tony Coleman, e-mail

Have Your Say

HE HAS BEEN hailed as the Messiah, come to save English football from another forty years of hurt. And from day one, **Fabio Capello** whipped his team into shape, banning booze and WAGS before a game, and controversially denying David Beckham his 100th cap. The fans threw themselves behind the Italian's new regime and were rewarded with a fantastic lacklustre win against mediocre Swiss opposition.

But what did YOU think of the man? We went on the streets to gauge the opinion of the England fans...

Fabi-oh yes...

or Fabi-oh no?
Is it thumbs up or thumbs down for Capello?

...English football is safe in Fabio's hands. I was only disappointed that Gordon Brown didn't announce Capello's knighthood the second Jenus scored in the 40th minute.

Carlton Suitcase, Walsall

...awarding Capello a knighthood after Jenus's goal would probably have been a little premature and would have smacked of the PM jumping on the bandwagon. An OBE would have been a more suitable reward for the first goal, with perhaps a CBE being awarded when Wright-Phillips put the game beyond doubt in the second half.

Bickerton Waddington, Cheshire

...I was disgusted when Capello gave his post-match interview through an interpreter. How typical of an Italian to refuse to learn English. I have lived in Italy for 16 years and in all that time none of my neighbours have bothered learning English so they can understand me. Consequently I have to shout and point at things in shops.

Mrs Batt, Florence

...when I saw on TV that the FA had appointed a foreigner as the England manager, I was so incensed that I put my foot through the screen, and sent the FA the bill!

Doug Mengele, Leeds

...it is very risky having the England manager communicating with his team through an interpreter. It would be easy for opposing teams to hypnotise the interpreter and get him to tell England to play all wrong and score own goals.

Edna Cartspring, Dudley

...Capello bears a slight resemblance to the late Stephen Milligan MP. Having a manager who vaguely resembles a transvestite tory who wanked himself to death in a binbag is hardly going to inspire the team to success in the forthcoming World Cup qualifiers.

Franklyn Wormwood, Hull

...Ron Greenwood, Graham Taylor, Steve McClaren and now this clown. Is it so difficult to appoint a decent England football manager? I think the entire FA committee should be put on the sex offenders register and their names and addresses made public.

Pontious Muldoon, Knightsbridge

...the FA have made the wrong choice in Fabio Capello, simply because neither his name, nationality nor the shape of his head lend themselves easily to being lampooned as a vegetable in tabloid newspapers.

Ziblah Beersheba, Truro

...when I heard on Radio 5Live that Capello had failed to select David Beckham for the squad against Switzerland, I was incensed. However, my radio is too small to put my foot through, so I drove to the BBC radio studios and put my foot through Nicky Campbell instead. And sent the FA the bill!

Doug Mengele, Leeds

...a good manager needs to reward effort in order to get the best from his team. I am the manager of a shoe shop, and my employee of the month gets a discount of 50% off any pair of shoes they want (up to the value of £40) and a free tin of polish. Perhaps if Capello did the same, awarding the man of the match a 50% discount off some shoes (up to the value of £40) and a free tin of polish, he may inspire them to give their best for England.

Nick Turdbridge, Wakefield

...Capello dosen't compare to the best manager England ever had, Sir Alf Ramsey. In my opinion, the FA should have appointed Most Haunted's Derek Acorah, himself an ex-footballer, as the manager. He could have contacted Ramsey in spirit world and put his tactical genius to use in matches.

Bartram Delacore, Leeds

...what Mr Delacore (above vox pop) forgets is that Mr Acorah can only communicate with denizens of the astral plane via his Red Indian guide Sam. Red Indians do not play football, and consequently do not have words for 'offside trap', 'throw-in', 'indirect free-kick and many more. Confusion could easily arise.

Hector Brightwell, Totnes

...apart from the language barrier, a much more worrying risk could arise from having the medium Derek Acorah as the England manager. As any viewer of Most Haunted could attest, Derek is constantly getting possessed by hostile spirits such as highwaymen, hanged murderers and the like. Should one of these spirits get control of him during during a half-time talk, the consequences don't bear thinking about.

Hazelnut Monkbottle, Wells

...once during Most Haunted Live in Stratford upon Avon, a spoon flew from behind a cameraman and just missed Yvette Fielding's ear. Should similar unexplained poltergeist activity manifest itself in the changing room, the spoon could easily hit Wayne Rooney in the eye, putting him out of action and jeopardising the World Cup campaign.

Hector Littlecress, Bury

...whilst I understand Mr Littlecress' concerns (above vox pop), the FA could simply appoint Uri Geller as number 2 to Derek Acorah. Uri could bend all the spoons in the dressing room before a match by rubbing them gently between his thumb and forefinger, thus rendering them harmless.

Chesney Piles, Redditch

IVAN the TERRIBLE

RUSSIA, IN THE SIXTEENTH CENTURY

IVAN CHETVYORTY VASILYEVICH, WE HEREBY CROWN YOU IVAN IV OF RUSSIA, GRAND PRINCE OF MOSCOW.

THERE GOES THE ANGLO-RUSSIAN TRADING AGREEMENT!

OH! THE CROWN HAS SLIPPED OVER MY EYES ~ I CAN'T SEE!

HE'S TRODDEN ON THE ENGLISH AMBASSADOR'S FOOT!

NOW HE'S SPILT COFFEE ALL OVER THE NEW REFORMS OF THE MUSCOVY LEGAL SYSTEM

WHOOPS! WHAT HAVE I DONE NOW?

BUMP

OH HE'S HOPELESS, ISN'T HE?

DREADFUL. A COMPLETE AMATEUR.

SUCKING

The Black Hole Truth

IN THEIR quest to understand how the universe started, the world's top boffins at the CERN Large Hadron Collider may inadvertently be about to create a BLACK HOLE that will *TURN THE WORLD INSIDE OUT!*

But what exactly are black holes, and why are they so dangerous? We asked former D:Ream keyboards player-turned high energy particle physics egghead *PROFESSOR BRIAN COX.*

"A black hole is a body of matter that exerts a fantastic gravitational pull, sucking things into itself," said Cox, whose song *Things Can Only Get Better* reached the top of the charts in 1994. "The more things it sucks in, the more powerful it gets. It's a bit like the opposite of a Dyson vacuum cleaner."

"If the CERN accelerator makes a black hole there will be nothing that anybody can do to stop it. Turning the machine off will be impossible, as the power switch will be one of the first things to get sucked into the vortex," added the electro-synth king.

And Cox, who played the mini-moog solo on *UR The Best Thing,* which made the Top Ten on its second re-release, had more bad news. "What's even more worrying is that scientists wouldn't even know they'd made a black hole in the first place, since they are so dense that not even light can escape from their gravitational fields. If we accidentally made one in the collider we wouldn't be able to see it," added the former D:Ream ivory tinkler whose hits dried up in the 90s.

WHEN THE UK gets sucked inside out by the CERN black hole, it will be a very different place to the one we know today.

The streets will be strewn with carpets and furniture as houses suddenly find their rooms on the outside. Hungry zoo animals will roam our towns when their cages turn back to front. Meanwhile our supermarket aisles will be a mess, as rice pudding, beans and noodle doodles get sucked out of their tins by the awesome cosmic power of the black hole and splashed all over the floor.

HOLE LOT OF TROUBLE: The nightmare that awaits the UK.

And people will fare no better. Men, women and children will be horrified to find their internal organs sucked onto the outside of their bodies, whilst their skin and faces are trapped helplessly on the inside.

It's a terrifying prospect for all of us, but it's even worse for the stars. With their glamorous lifestyles, matinee idol looks and multi-million pound endorsement deals, they have so much more to lose than the average man in the street.

How will they cope when they suddenly find themselves sucked inside out? We asked a selection of A-listers what they plan to do when the black hole strikes.

How the Stars will Cope

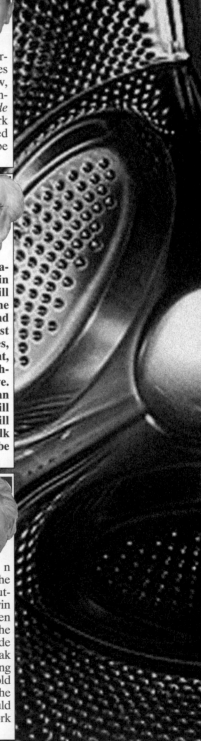

KERRY KATONA.........

"I'M dreading the Large Hadron Collider experiment spiralling out of control," the former Atomic Kitten mime-artist confessed to us last night. "I'm sure Iceland wouldn't want me advertising their sausages with all my intestines on show! I'm already working on a new, no-holds-barred fly-on-the-wall documentary series called *Kerry and Mark - Inside Out*, all about me and my husband Mark going bankrupt with our organs situated on the outside of our bodies. It should be on MTV in the autumn."

ROWAN WILLIAMS...

ARCHBISHOP of Canterbury Dr Rowan Williams thinks that being turned inside out will raise some interesting theological questions about the nature of being and his relationship with God. "The Lord is within all of us, so being turned inside out will in a sense bring His spirit out into the world to live amongst us," he said. "And in addition, we will, perhaps for the first time be able to truly see inside ourselves, which as a Christian, is very important, because only from looking for God within ourselves, can we really know His love. Of course, being inside out will mean that everything is reversed which will have enormous consequences. Shit will come out of our mouths and we will talk through our arses so, for me, it will be business as usual."

NOEL EDMONDS.........

"THE earth and everything on it turning inside out is a particularly horrifying prospect for me," said tidy bearded *Swapshop* star Noel Edmonds. "It means that the boxes on my show *Deal or No Deal* will have the amounts of money displayed on the outside, so all the scum contestants will win the jackpot prize of £250,000. Also, when the banker rings, I won't be able to hear the phone because my ears will be on the inside of my head." And things look equally bleak for Edmonds's most famous havoc-causing pink and yellow creation. A TV insider told us: "If Mr Blobby was turned inside out he would cease to be funny as people would see that inside he was just an out of work actor trying to make ends meet."

HELL!

e in Black Hole Britain

BILL ODDIE...........

THE world turning inside out is going to make life extra tough for curmudgeonly TV twitcher Bill Oddie. The scowling *SpringWatch* presenter told us: "I'm not going to be able to watch birds anymore, because when the black hole turns my birdwatching hide inside out, I'll be visible to them and they'll fly off. Also, with my internal organs on show, I'm likely to be mistaken for roadkill and attacked by carrion crows."

FERN BRITTON.....

A BLACK hole turning the world about face would spell disaster for daytime TV host and Ryvita ad queen Fern Britton. An ITV insider confessed: "Fern is very worried about the Large Hadron Collider. Being sucked inside out by a black hole would mean that her gastric band, the strap around the outside of her stomach which led to her new slim look, would be on the inside. Here it would have no effect and Fern would quickly find herself ballooning back to her old weight."

PHIL OAKEY...........

HUMAN League frontman Phil Oakey admitted that he was worried by the prospect of a black hole armageddon. "Me and the group being turned inside out is going to be very confusing for our fans. When the girls are on stage, no-one will know which is the dark-haired one and which is the blonde, since their trade mark barnets will be on the inside. It'll even be confusing for me, and I was married to one of them! I think it was the dark-haired one." And Phil voiced concern that this confusion could have an impact on the success of their latest album *Golden Hour of the Future*. "I don't think it's too much of an exaggeration to say that the effects of a black hole could cut sales of the new album in half," he told us. "We could be looking at single figures."

Have Your Say

THE HADRON COLLIDER is the most ambitious scientific project ever conceived, on a par with the Apollo Moonshot programme and the Human Genome Project. If it works, it will open up new horizons of scientific understanding.

But is it really worth the £4billion we have been forced to cough up for it? Could the money have been better spent keeping our old people warm this winter, building homes for tramps, or buying some more castles for her Majesty the Queen? We went on the streets to find out what *YOU* thought.

...THE scientists involved all seem very excited at the prospect of this experiment, but £4billion is a lot of money. Perhaps they should have paid for it themselves, raising money by doing a sponsored walk, organising a Bring and Buy sale or washing their neighbours' cars.

Howard Jones, electrician

...£4billion just to make a machine that creates a black hole to swallow up the earth? What a waste of money. They should do something useful for a change and invent a black hole that sucks in paedophiles.

H Timberarse, plumber

...WITH reference to the previous letter. Mr Timberarse fails to realise that a black hole which sucks in paedophiles will not solve the paedophile problem. They will simply go through a worm hole in the fabric of time and end up putting children in other dimensions at risk.

J Lumberjack, pharmacist

...THE technology needed to create this machine is awe-inspiring, and the only thing they can think to do with it is to smash protons into each other. Why do they always have to break things? Why can't they keep the protons nice?

Edna Balloons, housewife

...MY doctor tells me that at 46 stone I have to lose weight. But now some of the greatest minds in the world working on the Hadron Collider tell us that they don't really know what weight is. Well I might as well carry on eating cakes until they find out.

B Frampton, driving instructor

...WHY is it called the LARGE Hadron Collider? Why not just the Hadron Collider? I'll tell you why, because it's been built by men and they are obsessed with the size of their cocks. Hadron even sounds like HARD-ON. It's just cocks, cocks, cocks with men. Cocks, cocks, cocks, it is, really. Cocks, cocks, cocks, cocks, cocks!

Germaine Greer, harridan

...THEY needn't have spent all that money. If they wanted to get two protons to collide they should have tied one on the bumper of my wife's car and the other to the back wall of our garage. Ha! Ha! Ha! It's a cracker!

Frank Carson, comedian

...WITH reference to the previous letter. I'm afraid that Mr Carson has shown his failure to grasp the concept of how the Large Hadron Collider works. His wife would have to drive her car into the garage at just under the speed of light and with an incredible degree of accuracy in order for the experiment to be a success.

Hector Albany, physicist

...SCIENTISTS needn't worry about a black hole swallowing up the earth. There is already a massive, incredibly dense body threatening civilasation. My mother in law. Ha! Ha! Ha! It's the way I tell 'em.

Frank Carson, comedian

...HONESTLY, it's just cocks, cocks, cocks, cocks cocks, cocks, cocks!

Germaine Greer, harridan

Black Hole Blackpool

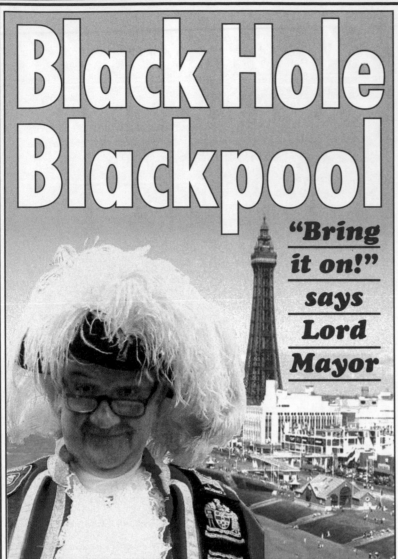

"Bring it on!" says Lord Mayor

BLACKPOOL'S FAMOUS illuminations could lose some of their sparkle this year - that's if scientists' fears of a black hole forming at the Large Hadron Collider come true. For the infinitely dense body in the Swiss research facility would create a gravitational field so strong that not even the lights of the seaside resort's world famous winter attraction could resist its pull.

"The light would all be sucked straight out of the bulbs towards Switzerland," said Lord Mayor Ivan Taylor. "And whilst that would be good news for people standing on the town side of the display, anybody looking from the beach or the pier would think there had been a power cut."

SPECTACULAR

The town's tourist chiefs admit that this could spell disaster for Blackpool, which relies heavily on its spectacular light show to attract visitors from all over the country. And at a press conference held in the town hall, Alderman Taylor outlined the council's 10-point plan to keep the lights shining in the event of a black hole. The measures the council are considering include:

• **REPLACING** red bulbs in the illuminations display with blue ones, as the shorter blue wavelength photons have less mass and are less likely to be pulled towards the black hole.

• **PLACING** mirrors on buildings along the Golden Mile to double the effectiveness of the light before it gets sucked to Switzerland.

• **MAKING** greater use of non-incandescent decorations such as tinsel, glitter and luminous paint.

EXCLUSIVE

Taylor accepts that if a point of infinite density does indeed form in the Collider, his town's illuminations may not be as much of a draw as they have been in previous years. But he was remaining light-hearted about the physicists' doomsday scenario.

MONOCULAR

He told reporters: "Blackpool was blacked out from 1939 till 1945 and it didn't do anything to spoil the fun in Lancashire's premier coastal holiday destination."

BINOCULAR

"We're not going to let a little thing like the catastrophic effects of a black hole dampen our spirits, and we're facing the prospect with typical Blackpool humour," he said. "We're updating our traditional solid black 'Blackpool by Night' postcards to read 'Blackpool All The Time'. And we'll also be producing a new range of saucy postcards, all relying heavily on the suggestive possibilities of the words 'black hole', and featuring scotsmen in kilts, young ladies in nudist camps and newly-wed couples in bed and breakfasts," he added.

INVISIBLE SUN

Sting's Mission to Explain Black Hole Collider in Song

POP arsehole **STING** is set to explain the mysteries of particle physics... in song! In his new single *Mountains of Colliding Hearts*, the former bass player with 80s boy-band THE POLICE explains what happens when protons from a hydrogen atom are smashed into each other at the speed of light at the Large Hadron Collider.

He told *Radio 1 Newsbeat*'s Jackie Quimfest: "When I saw the CERN cyclotron on one of my very large widescreen televisions - I think it's 105", possibly more - anyway, it's the biggest one you can get, I know that - I was immediately fascinated. I started thinking about this 17-mile-long machine, the Large Hadron Collider, which is looking for something unimaginably small - even tinier than a hundred & thousand."

PARTICLE

"The Higgs Boson - the so-called "God Particle" - is the missing link between the Big Bang, Steven Hawkins and Einstein's Theory of Relativity," he continued. "It is literally the Holy Grail for scientists who

are researching Quantum Physics, String Theory and that. And when I started thinking about it, the idea for the new song just came to me."

QUANTUM

"It's a number all about the relationships between the different particles in an atom - the proteins, the croutons, the quarks and the gluons. They are unable to love each other until they realise that the fundamental forces in the nucleus that are trying to tear them apart are also what's holding them together," Sting said.

"It's a soft-rock ballad with jazzy overtones," he added.

The single comes hard on the heels of *The Large Hadron Rap* - a light-hearted song produced by scientists working at the CERN Collider, which became an unexpected internet hit last month. Sting told

us: "My record's better than theirs, because I'm treating the subject of String Theory with the seriousness it deserves. Not only that, but I've got the scientific expertise to back up my music with meaningful lyrics that will make people think."

DOUBLE

"And if I don't step up to the plate to explain these subjects to the ignorant public, then who will?" the big twat continued. "I play the bass, guitar and lute, so string theory doesn't phase me at all. And I'm also no slouch when it comes to big bangs, as I poke my missus Trudi Styler for five hours every single night."

Sting's previous single was an attempt to express musically the solution to Fermat's Last Theorem. *Searching for an Answer (to the Theorem of Love)*, which he recorded with fellow pop dickhead Bono,

failed to chart when it was released in the same week as *Integers of the Heart (Ain't No Solution)* by pop wankstain Alex James out of Blur.

TODAY we take pornographic films for granted. Whether we're downloading them from the internet, buying them from the shelves of our local sex shop, or borrowing them from an overweight, sweaty man at work, they are part and parcel of our lives.

Erotic films are big business. But have you ever stopped to think how they are made? Let's take a fascinating peek behind the scenes of the adult entertainment industry to discover...

How a PORNOGRAPHIC FILM is Made

◀ **MAKING** a pornographic film is a long, laborious process. Indeed, it can often be several days after the director gets his first scene "in the can" before the finished movie hits the shops. But, just like any other production, a skin-flick starts with a written screenplay. This will have a carefully-worked plot, convincing dialogue and strong characters, just like any other script. But in the bongo film business, there's an extra element... plenty of red hot pumping sex action! Here, a SCRIPT-WRITER is working on his screenplay for *Cum Guzzling Sluts vol 7*. He is putting the finishing touches to a scene featuring lesbian rimming, a DP, triple cock oral and gonzo gang bang facials.

▶ **LATER THAT** morning, the finished script for *Cum Guzzling Sluts vol 7* drops onto the PRODUCER's desk. It's almost identical to its extremely successful predecessor *Cum Guzzling Sluts vol 6*, but this time the action is even hotter. The producer knows he has a winner on his hands and decides that *CGS7*, as it now becomes known, should be committed to celluloid. The producer is a busy man, as he currently has around 24 different porno film projects on the go. But he will be actively involved in this production, as a lot of the sex scenes will be shot on location in his house, at the side of his swimming pool or across the bonnet of his Porsche. His first responsibility is to appoint a director.

◀ **THIS** is the DIRECTOR; a veteran of over 5,000 previous porn movies, he was also responsible for *Cum Guzzling Sluts vols 1 to 6*. When he gets his copy of the script, it is the director's responsibility to bring the words on the page to life on screen. He must think carefully about the characters, action and storyline before casting the actors who he thinks are best-suited to play the leading roles in this production. He gives the script a cursory glance before phoning up the same three blokes and six girls who appear in all his films. And his luck is in; they are all available immediately, so filming can get underway with a minimum of delay. *CGS7* has a complicated plot with a lot of different set-ups, and could take the whole morning to shoot.

▲ **FILMING** is about to begin. On set in the producer's kitchen, the ACTORS prepare for their tricky opening scene - an erotically-charged anal gang bang culminating in a Belgian spit-roast and double facial cum-shot. All the crew are gathered - the cameraman, the lighting engineer, the sound recordist, the director and the assistant director. The room is pretty crowded as there are also film crews from Bravo, NutsTV and Virgin1 all shooting behind-the-scenes documentaries about the making of a porn film. Everyone is ready and the actors are raring to go, so it's lights, camera... hardcore porn action!

CONTINUED OVER

SHOOTING starts with the assistant director operating a **CLAPPER-BOARD** - a device used on film sets at the beginning of every "take" to ensure that the sound and the pictures can be synchronised in post-production. This means that the actors' grunts, gasps, moans and orgasmic howls coincide accurately with their pelvic thrusts, shudders and facial gurnings. Words written on the board tell the editor which scene is being filmed, helping to prevent continuity errors that might spoil the narrative arc of the film.

The **CAMERAMAN** has one of the most difficult jobs on the set. He must frame each shot according to the director's wishes, supervise and approve the position of the lights, and ensure that his camera is focused and running correctly. A pornographic film cameraman also has to to be agile, as he will be required to crouch in awkward positions for long periods in order to get his lens right up close to the action... so his viewers will be able to really see it going in.

THE SOUND RE-CORDIST's job is to catch on tape the sex noises during the action scenes as well as the dialogue in between. The unsung hero of the set, his careful work often goes unnoticed. This is because purchasers of pornographic films usually watch them with the sound off so they don't wake up their wives upstairs. On the rare occasions when the volume is turned up, such as when she's gone to the shops, viewers invariably fast-forward through the dull bits between the sex scenes anyway.

MAKING a film is very much a stop-start business. Filming can be interrupted for many reasons - loading fresh film into the camera, removing a foreign body from the camera lens, or a documentary film crew from Granada Men & Motors turning up late. And during these interruptions, the male lead can easily lose focus... and his erection! Waiting for him to "get wood" again means further costly delays; it could even lead to shooting running over into the afternoon when the producer's house is needed for the filming of *Barely Legal Anal 4*. To avoid this, most porn shoots employ **FLUFFERS** - women whose job it is to keep the actors from going soft by performing 'treading water' style fellatio on them during these frequent on-set interruptions. Here, a couple of fluffers arrive for work on their scooter.

ALL THE shots are in the can but there is still a lot of work to do on the film. In the editing suite the various shots are assembled into their running order. It is the **EDITOR**'s responsibility to whittle down nearly 130 minutes of raw footage into a finished 2-hour film, so he has to be ruthless. Here, he feels that one of the male leads has taken too long to bring himself to orgasm and ejaculate up his co-star's back. He decides that 2 whole minutes of back-scuttling and masturbation can be removed without adversely affecting *CGS7*'s plot, and so the scene hits the cutting room floor. But nothing goes to waste, and that footage is kept in case the next film he'll be working on, *Cum Guzzling Sluts vol 8*, runs a bit short.

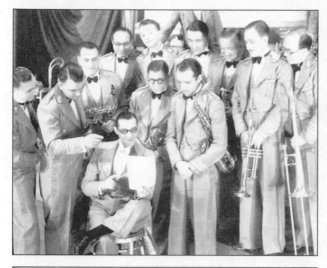

THE SCORE is a very important part of any movie sound track. Music helps to set the scene and create the mood essential to drive the narrative along. And a pornographic film is no different. Here, members of the STUDIO ORCHESTRA study the sheet music which has been composed to complement the action in CGS7. A few seconds later, every member of the band except the drummer, the slap-bass player and the organist go home.

IN ORDER to sell, CGS7 must stand out from its competitors on the sex shop shelf, and this means having the right packaging. At a meeting with his DESIGNERS, the producer explains that featuring a picture of the pasty boilers who are actually in the film on the cover could kill sales of the DVD stone dead. So it is decided that the box should instead feature a montage of glamorous, tanned, silicone-enhanced American porn stars lifted off the internet.

THE porn industry has a global market, and it greatly increases the profitability of a film if it can be sold abroad. Here, an ACTOR dubs the grunts, groans and pillow talk from CGS7 into German.

IT'S ALL systems go as the first copies of CGS7 roll off the production line at the DVD plant. They are then taken to the warehouse from where they are dispatched to sex shops around the country. Distribution is a complex logistical process and this means that it could be anything up to 3 days before the film is available to the general public. However, a few lucky viewers will get their hands on a copy sooner than that, thanks to the FORK LIFT TRUCK DRIVER who has pocketed a copy and will be selling poor quality VHS knock-offs in his local pub that same night.

THE DVD has been on sale for a week, and it's time for the money men to tot up the figures and see how it has been selling. Here the producer meets with his ACCOUNTANTS. The good news is that CGS7 has taken even more than CGS6. In its first week on general release, it has grossed £8,000 across the tills. But that's not all profit by any means. After paying the wages of the cast and crew, the producer is left with a meagre £7,800.

SO THAT'S how a pornographic film is made. Next time your wife nips round to her sister's and you take the opportunity to grab a box of tissues and settle down in your favourite chair to enjoy a scud flick, take a few moments to remember the many talented people whose hard work made your wank possible.

|||||||||||||||||||||||||||||||||||||||||||||||||||||||||||

NEXT WEEK *We Go Behind the Scenes at a Bell Casting Foundry*

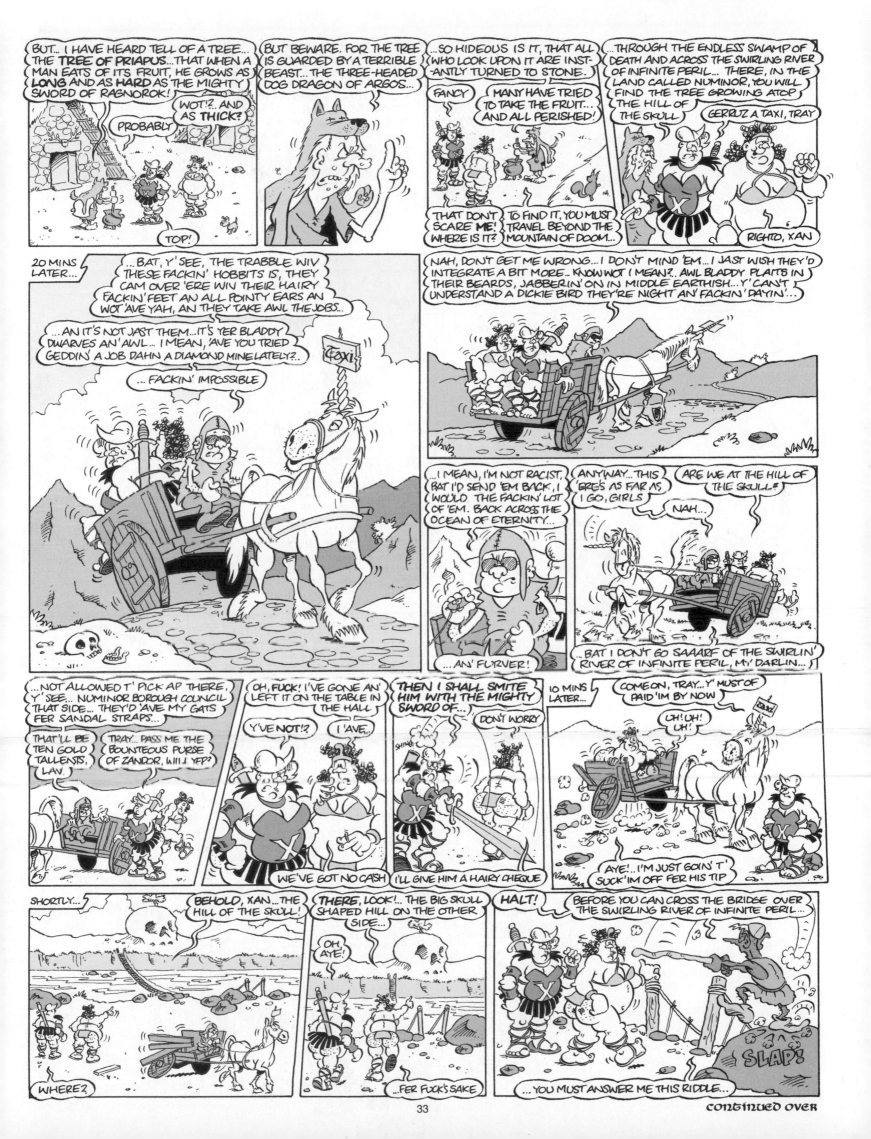

CONTINUED OVER

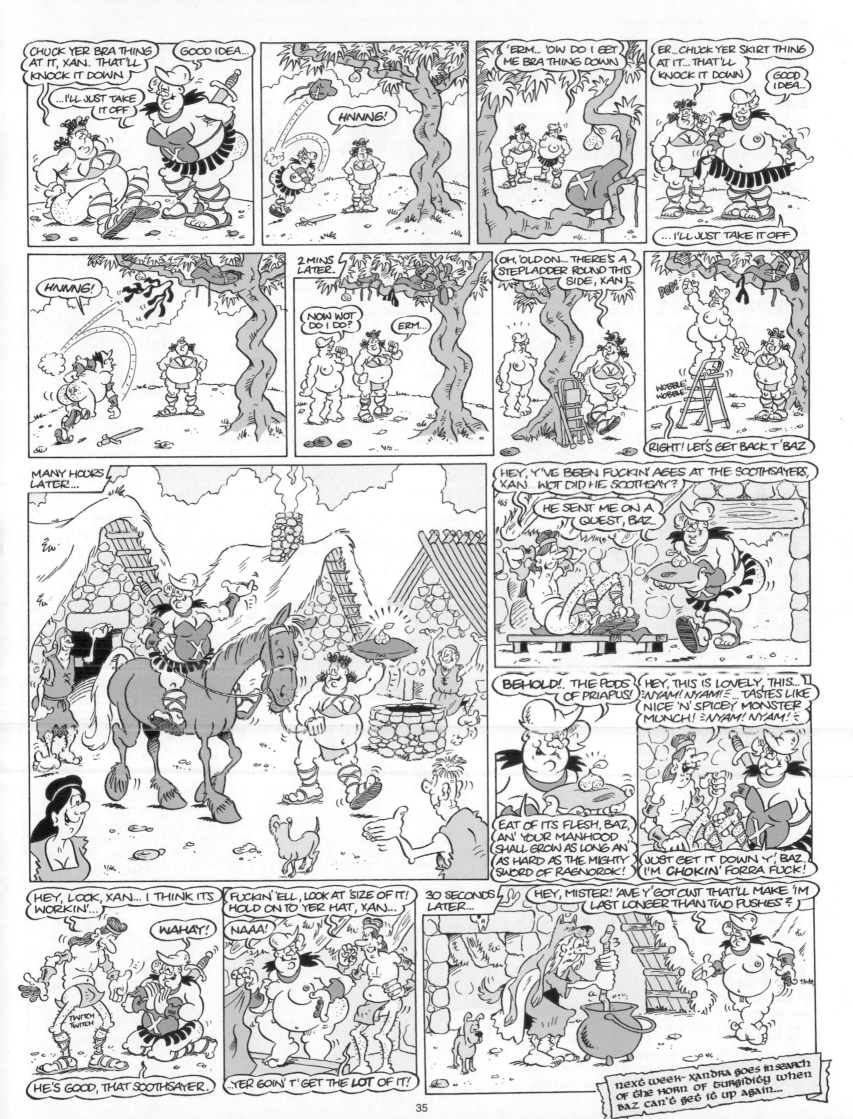

LETTERBOCKS

Viz Comic, PO Box 656
North Shields, NE30 4XX
e-mail: letters@viz.co.uk

STAR LETTER

■ According to Sainsbury's latest TV ad, they 'only sell Fairtrade bananas'. That's all very well, but it means everyone will have to go somewhere else for the rest of their shopping.

Sid Raisins, Email-on-Sea

Monarchy in the UK

■ I think it's a wonderful idea making our teenagers take an oath of allegiance to the Queen. It would teach them respect for other people and would stop anti-social behaviour. They do it in American schools every morning and there's no crime there.

Doris Ludford, Claxby

■ Being interviewed on Radio 2's *Steve Wright Show*, Piers Morgan complained that every time he flies first class, he finds the caviar the air stewards serve him is too salty. Well, I for one am at a complete loss as to why this might be.

M Winner, London

■ My grandchildren bought me a pedigree Siamese kitten for my birthday last year. It was a beautiful little thing, but sadly at about sixteen weeks old it started to develop orange tabby stripes on its back legs. So I had it put to sleep.

Edna Spridlington, Hull

■ How about a picture of a big dog in a wheelbarrow?

J Geils, Luton

No problem.

■ What a load of rubbish these modern so-called comedy programmes are these days. They are usually full of swearing and filth and are just not funny. What ever happened to proper comedies, like the one set in that shop with the shit-stabber and the woman with the blue hair who was always always talking about her cunt?

Mabel Cuxwold, Hartlepool

■ I agree with Mrs Cuxwold *(previous letter)* when she says that the old comedies were the best. I used to like the racist ones, like the night school full of foreigners who couldn't speak English, or the one where that horrible black man moved in next door to that poor white couple.

Mavis Minting, London

■ I saw a man putting a plastic bag of dogshit in a bin on a lamp post the other day. A sign on the bin read 'Advertise Your Business Here.' Well, I for one cannot think of a business that could possibly benefit from an association with bins of dogshit on lamp posts.

T Thorn, Tynemouth

■ I was interested to see that the Vatican has updated its list of 7 Deadly Sins for the first time since they were introduced 1,500 years ago in an attempt to bring Catholic doctrine into the 21st century. Particularly pleasing was their environmental stance, insisting that those who use and do not recycle carrier bags are bound for hell. However, I was disappointed to see that they neglected to include collaborating with the Nazis and covering up systematic child abuse. Perhaps they'll get round to those in 3,500 AD.

T Goole, Leeds

■ On the same subject, the Vatican have decided to include 'amassing obscene wealth' in their list of revised sins. It's a good job that they haven't included hypocrisy in the list or they'd be doubly fucked.

T Aquinas, Gateshead

■ My granny is 85-years-young and has more energy than many people half her age. On a recent trip to New Zealand, she astonished everybody by deciding to do a bungee jump from a bridge 300 feet above a gorge. We all thought that she had bitten off more than she could chew this time and we were right. She dislocated both hips, broke her pelvis, and suffered two detached retinas and a torn diaphragm. However, she was undeterred and has vowed to do a free-fall parachute jump next year.

Glenda Claxby, Lincoln

■ Why doesn't the Archbishop of Canterbury just bend over and put his hat on his arse?

Frank Laddercoin, Cheam

■ According to Sheryl Crow, "Everybody's makin' love, 'cause makin' love comes for free." Not on Canal Road in Bradford, it doesn't. It costs £30. £35 if you want tits at the same time.

Mark Mallinson, e-mail

■ What is it with women newsreaders? They shouldn't be allowed. In my opinion, Natasha Kaplinsky, Fiona Bruce and their ilk should be in the newsroom kitchens at the BBC, making cups of tea for the men newsreaders.

Major-Gen. G Hepscott-Black Aldershot

■ On a radio advert for the blood transfusion service, Sharon Osbourne says: "Somebody out there gave blood and saved my life." When I heard this, it really got me thinking, and I decided there and then not to give blood any more.

JR Tuk, e-mail

■ I was heartened to see recently that Lesley Ash was given a £5million compensation payout after contracting an infection whilst in hospital. All too often I see the NHS squandering my hard-earned taxes saving the

Biscuit Barrel

how ironic it would have been if they were digestives. It would certainly have been worth a letter in this column.

Margaret Toft, Spridlington

● I LOVE biscuits. So much so that I wrote a poem about them.

*If I did have some biscuits,
Oh, happy would I be,
From their tin I would take them,
And dunk them in my tea.*

That's as far as I've got at the moment, but I'm working on the next verse. The second line ends in 'eat' and the fourth line ends in 'treat'. I'm just filling in the gaps.

Andrew Motion, London

● WHY DON'T Crawfords make their Cheddar biscuits two-inches thick? I am morbidly obese, and I love to shove a quarter of a packet in my mouth at once. My work colleagues say it makes me look uncouth and greedy, and I find this hurtful. They wouldn't be able to say this if I was eating a single, albeit two-inch thick, biscuit.

Kevin Bellend, Heartford

● I LIKE to eat biscuits whilst on the toilet. My favourite are Jaffa Cakes, as they are easy to get out of the packet using one hand - particularly important if you have already started wiping.

Morgan Cheeseborough, e-mail

● WHEN OH WHEN are the manufacturers of Ritz crackers going to put salt on the underside of the biscuit rather that the top? I for one am fed up of having to turn my Ritzes upside down before putting them on my tongue.

Barney Snitterby, Louth

● ARE NICE biscuits pronounced Nice or Nice? I always pronounce it Nice, but my wife insists that it is Nice.

Barry Macbeth, Barnes

I'm afraid your wife is right, Mr Macbeth. It is pronounced Nice.

● I HAD TO LAUGH the other day. My young son ate so many biscuits that he gave himself indigestion. What type of biscuits were they? Unfortunately, they were Rich Tea biscuits, but

36

lives of people who I've never even heard of. What a refreshing change it is to have this money going to Lesley, especially since her self-inflicted swollen lips have ruined her chances of getting any more lucrative advertising work on the telly.

J Townshend, Nottingham

■ Political correctness has gone too far. These days I am expected to get permission off my own wife before I make love to her. Well it seems a shame to wake her up.

T Chipboard, Hove

■ How about a CGI picture of a bloke kissing that bird's arse? I've knocked one up for you in case you haven't got one.

Nathan Jenkinson, e-mail

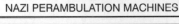

You Ask, I Flannel

Your Ecclesiastical Questions Waffled Over by the Archbishop of Canterbury

Dr. Rowan Williams

Dear Archbishop,

I HAVE SEEN the cherubs they have in Heaven in lots of paintings and it seems to me that they tend to be rather fat babies and have very small wings. They are going to have to flap them at a fair old rate to keep themselves flying. This being the case, I was wondering if, like bees, they make a buzzing sound as they flit from cloud to cloud? I hope not, as this buzzing would certainly impair my enjoyment of the hereafter, especially if I was there for all eternity.

D Holloway, Jesmond

Dear Mr Holloway,
I wouldn't worry. Don't forget that Heaven is high in the sky on top of the clouds where there is very little gravity. Cherubs may only have to flap their wings very slowly in order to fly, and they may make a very low noise, like a moth. And you can only hear moths when they come right by your ear.

✝✝✝✝✝✝✝✝✝✝✝✝✝✝✝

Dear Archbishop,

I WAS AT an art gallery recently, and I saw a painting set in Heaven where a lot of cherubims and seraphims were playing a fanfare on trumpets. In your previous answer, you said that Heaven is very high up in the sky. It is my understanding that at very great altitude the air is very thin, and that this would make the trumpets sound very high-pitched, a bit like speeded-up kazoos. Well, what sort of a way is that to serenade the Father of all creation?

C Wilson, Ealing

Dear Miss Wilson,
I have a great and unshakeable faith that the trumpets in heaven resonate at a lower frequency than our earthbound trumpets do. This compensates for the thin heavenly atmosphere that would, ordinarily, lead to the high-pitched fanfare you describe. What you have to remember is, these heavenly hosts have been playing brass instruments for God since the dawn of time, so I am sure they have ironed all the wrinkles out by now!

✝✝✝✝✝✝✝✝✝✝✝✝✝✝✝

Dear Archbishop,

ON A RECENT visit to the Vatican's Cistine Chapel, I couldn't help noticing that there was an awful lot of nudity going on in heaven. Now I'm rather old fashioned, and I don't really like the idea of having to go completely bare in the hereafter. Would it, do you think, be possible for me and my husband to keep our clothes on in Heaven?

Mrs Edna Snitterby, Toft next Newton

Dear Miss Snitterby,
Unfortunately for you, I believe that there is a very strictly enforced "no clothes" rule in Heaven. The reason for this is simple. People have been dying for thousands of years, and if everyone was allowed to wear their own clothes, you'd have people walking round in doublets and hoses, caveman animal skins, Victorian top hats and astronaut suits all at the same time. People from the olden days would covet modern things like zips, velcro fastenings and trainers and end up having to go to Hell. No, it's better all round if everyone is naked. But I'm sure that God would not want you to feel uncomfortable or embarrassed. It is unlikely that he would raise any objection to you wearing a towel or even fleshlings for the first few days of your eternal stay.

✝✝✝✝✝✝✝✝✝✝✝✝✝✝✝

Dear Archbishop,

I NOTICED in a painting of the Annunciation, that the Archangel Gabriel had rather large wings compared to his body size, which when folded were visible over the top of his head, a bit like Brian Blessed's in *Flash Gordon*. I was just wondering what sort of noise they make when he takes off.

D Holloway, Jesmond

Dear Mr Holloway,
I have searched deep into my soul and prayed for guidance on this question, and I am now firmly of the belief that his wings will sound like someone opening and closing an umbrella.

"That's all I've got time for this week, religion fans. But if you've got any ecumenical questions you want waffled on about but not really answered, then write to me at: **The A. B. of C, Viz Comic, PO Box 656, North Shields NE30 4XX"**

Rowan

RICHARD LITTLEJOHN of DAILY MAIL FARM
Prop: Farmer Paul Dacre

LISTEN HERE, LITTLEJOHN. I'M OFF INTO TOWN TO BUY MYSELF A NEW SOLID GOLD TOP HAT. AND I'M LEAVING YOU IN CHARGE OF THE DAILY MAIL READERS WHILE I'M GONE.
YESSIR, FARMER DACRE. THANK YOU SIR.

THESE READERS ARE MY LIVELIHOOD, LITTLEJOHN. SO TAKE GOOD CARE OF THEM...
...OR ELSE I'll HAVE YOUR BALLS BOILED FOR BREAKFAST!
GULP! YESSIR!
CLUCK! TUT! CLUCK! EEH! TSK!

HERE YOU ARE, LITTLE OLD BIDDIES. HAVE THESE TASTY ARTICLES ABOUT A POSSIBLE LINK BETWEEN IMMIGRATION AND CANCER
EEH! TUT! CLUCK!
SEND 'EM ALL BACK

WOAH! THAT HUNGRY FOX HAS GOT HIS BEADY EYE ON OUR PLUMP, JUICY DAILY MAIL READERS
CLUCK!
I'D BETTER SHOO HIM OFF OR HE'LL GOBBLE THEM UP!

BLAM!
CLEAR OFF, Y'VERMIN!

HEH! THAT'S THE LAST WE'LL SEE OF OLD FOXY.
NOW I'll GO AND PREPARE SOME MORE DAILY MAIL READER FEED.

THERE. I'VE MIXED TOGETHER SOME OPINIONS ABOUT ASYLUM SEEKERS AND EUROPEAN FRUIT REGULATIONS INTO A NICE HYSTERICAL MUSH.
HELLO, THAT'S ODD — THE MAIL READERS HAVE GONE ALL QUIET OUTSIDE.

SO! THE SLY OLD FOX IS TRYING TO LURE THEM AWAY WITH THAT PICTURE OF A NEW ROYAL BABY
COOO! COOO!
EEH! COO!
HE'S GOT THEM TRANSFIXED IN A HYPNOTIC STATE

BLAM!
HA! THAT'S BROKEN THE SPELL!

COME ON, BIDDIES. YOU'D BETTER GET INTO THE COOP OUT OF HARM'S WAY.
EEH!
CLUCK! TUT! BWUK! BWUK!

THERE. THEY'LL BE SAFE NOW.
I'LL JUST TAKE A QUICK NAP.

SUDDENLY
SQUAWK! EEH! CLUCK!
SNORE... HUNH?! WHAT'S ALL THE COMMOTION?

BAH! THAT CUNNING FOX IS TRYING TO FORCE THE DAILY MAIL READERS OUT OF THEIR COOP, NOW!
LESBIAN & GAY DROP-IN CENTRE
24-HOUR GAY PARTIES
COOP FOR SALE
TUT! CLUCK! BWAAK! EEH! WELL! IT'S NOT RIGHT!
HE'S BUILT A LESBIAN AND GAY DROP-IN CENTRE NEXT DOOR, AND THE OLD BIDDIES ARE ALL MOVING OUT IN DISGUST.

CALM DOWN, BIDDIES. IT'S A TRICK! FOXY JUST WANTS TO GET HIS PAWS ON YOU, AND EAT YOU ALL UP!
CLUCK! CLUCK! EEH!
COME ALONG, GET BACK INTO THE COOP.

I'VE PADLOCKED THE DOOR THIS TIME, SO NO HARM CAN COME TO THEM.
CLUCK! B-WUK!
BRING BACK THE BIRCH!
NOW TO GET BACK TO MY NAP.

TIP TOE TIP TOE
ACME ISLAMIC FUNDAMENTALIST FANCY DRESS COSTUME ABU HAMZA
SNORE

AND
SNORE
ACME ISLAMIC FUNDAMENTALIST FANCY DRESS COSTUME ABU HAM

SHORTLY
YAWN AH, WELL. I'D BETTER GO AND CHECK TO SEE IF THE DAILY MAIL READERS HAVE LAID ANY EGGS.
I'LL NEED TO POP THEM INTO AN INCUBATOR SO THEY CAN HATCH INTO FLUFFY LITTLE MAIL-READING CHICKS.

HELLO BIDDIES! I'VE COME TO TAKE YOUR CHICKS!
BWAAAK?

WAH! WHY ARE YOU ATTACKING ME WITH YOUR HANDBAGS?
EEH!
TUT! BWAAK!
GET OFF—**OOF!**
EEH, THE POOR KIDDIES!

LATER
GROAN! WHAT HAPPENED...?
PAUL DACRE
LITTLEJOHN! THE COOP DOOR IS WIDE OPEN, AND ALL MY DAILY MAIL READERS HAVE BEEN EATEN BY A FOX!

AND SO
HURRY UP WITH THOSE DIPPY SOLDIERS, LITTLEJOHN.
PAUL DACRE
OOYAH YES, FARMER DACRE. WINCE
TAP TAP CRACK

Salad Daze for Albert

A CONFUSED, 108-year old Somme veteran was spending his first night behind bars last night after Walsall magistrates found him guilty of making two trips to the salad bar at a high street pizza restaurant. Albert Fairbrass, who won the George Cross for outstanding bravery in the trenches, was arrested when a fellow customer at Pizza World in Redditch reported him to the manager after he returned to the salad bar to top up his dish with greens for a second time.

Whistle-blower Mrs Edna Busybitch told the local newspaper: "It made my blood boil when I saw him helping himself to a second bowl of lettuce, so I called the waiter over and pointed out what he was up to."

She continued: "I don't care how old he is, or what he did in the First World War. It's the likes of him what puts the price of salad up for the rest of us law-abiding citizens. They can lock him up and throw away the key, for all I care."

SALADSCLUSIVE

AND

Police were called and the bewildered Chelsea Pensioner was taken to Redditch Police Station where he was questioned through the night, before being charged.

He appeared before magistrates later that day and was sentenced to six months in prison. His solicitor told us: "Mr Fairbrass suffers from chronic septic pleurisy after being gassed at Ypres and was recently told by his doctor that he had just four months to live. In the light of this information, we have decided not to lodge an appeal. There's already such a backlog of cases in the court system that any appeal wouldn't get heard till next year at the earliest, so frankly there's no point in us bothering to even set the wheels in motion."

IT

"Unfortunately, it looks like Mr Fairbrass will just have to die in prison," he added.

Other customers, who had gathered for Mr Fairbrass's birthday party, accused Pizza Palace staff of over-reacting, but manager Hector Bland was unrepentant. "The company has a stated policy of zero tolerance when it comes to diners breaking the single salad bar visit rule," he told us. "This is clearly written down in the Terms and Conditions section of our parent company's website."

THE

"If Mr Fairbrass had taken the trouble to visit that page and read through all the small-print, he would have been left in no doubt that he would face prosecution if he went back for seconds," he continued.

TO

"If we make an exception for one 108-year-old, terminally ill, confused, decorated war hero, we'd have to make them for everybody," he added.

Meanwhile, Albert himself was unavailable for comment. A prison spokesman told us: "Unfortunately, Mr Fairbrass is unable to come to the phone right now as he is being bummed in the showers by Mr Big."

 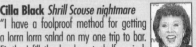

MEDDLESOME RATBAG

40

HISTORY COULD BE HISTORY

A HISTORY shortage is threatening to put thousands of academics out of work, a top professor claimed this week. According to the renowned Cambridge academic ALAN CLAXBY, it will soon be back to the future for historians as they run out of old stuff to study.

Professor Claxby told reporters: "As historians we have been living in fear of this day for many years. Time was I would be regaling you with an analysis of how Hitler came to power or why Augustus was the best Roman Emperor, but that's all been done. There's only so many books you can write about burning some cakes and Robert the Bruce watching a spider."

PRESENT

"At some point history had to become the present, and that point is now. History has finally caught up with us, it's 2008 and there's nothing old happening now. We've used up all our resources of the past and we're just left with the present."

According to the Professor, history officially goes from the pre-historic era, through the Stone Age, Iron Age, Medieval Age, Renaissance, etc, right up to yesterday teatime. "History runs out at midnight every day," Claxby told us. "This wasn't a problem until last month, when academics

HISTORICAL RANT: Claxby and some of the history he claims is now a thing of the past.

discovered that they had written something about everything that had happened so far, and that they had officially run out of old stuff."

"We'd been living on borrowed time," says Claxby. "History went on for ages and ages so we were all been able to get a fair few essays and books out of it, but nowadays history has pretty much happened and between us we've all had a theory about all of it. Job done."

PUDDING

Claxby and many fellow academics are due to descend on Parliament next week to lobby for more history. In response to their campaign, the Government have offered assurances that they will do their utmost to generate more notable incidents, a gesture that Claxby describes as 'too little too late'.

"They saw this coming. They made a perfunctory gesture at making history by introducing 24 hour drinking, creating super casinos and invading Iraq. But these were all lazy and ill thought through," said Claxby. If Gordon Brown had a fight with a Frenchman and got an arrow through his eye, or the Queen ordered the stabbing of the Archbishop of Canterbury, that would give us something to get our teeth into. This is crunch time, either give us some better events to cover or history could very well be history."

HUMPHRIES

Academics fear that unless the government comes up with some decent history quickly, they will be forced to study such underwhelming current events as the Spice Girls reunion, Amy Winehouse's Grammies and *Big Brother: Celebrity Hijack*, which Claxby believes is the worst series of *Big Brother* in the history of the programme.

In this month's *English Historical Review* he writes: "I think the trouble with this series was that none of the contestants

MODERN HISTORY: The Spice Girls yesterday.

had the charming stupidity of Brian, or the fascination that transexual Nadia held for the public. Of course, it didn't help that it was being broadcast on E4, but that fact in itself cannot be used to entirely excuse the terrible viewing figures – the dull selection of contestants must shoulder some of the blame."

43

STARTS HERE!

Harry Herring's Antique Shop of Mysteries...

Ah, good morning. I'm Harry Herring... Welcome to my Antique Shop of Mystery.

Please... step inside, don't be shy...

There's nothing inside that can harm you...

Well.

...at least, that's what one young man thought who came browsing my shelves 10 years ago to this very day...

Excuse me...

...how much for this old legbone?

This? This is the leg bone of the Marquis de Sade.

Wow!! No kidding?

It's true.

I sold the whole skeleton piece by piece...and everyone who bought one of his bones died in mysterious circumstances.

The man who bought the skull was bitten to death. A woman who bought the hands was found strangled...

...are you sure you want to buy it?

Ha! What superstitious nonsense!.......I'll take it. It's just what I want for my mantlepiece.

Very well, Sir. If you're sure.

The following day, police were called to a nearby flat where a grisly discovery had been made...

It's a mystery. He's been murdered, but the door was locked from the inside and there was no sign of a forced entry.

How was he killed, sir?

He was kicked up the arse, sergeant...

...kicked up the arse to death!

Kicked up the arse to death?..

...but by who? Or **what?**

The culprit was never found and no arrest was made. Perhaps there is a perfectly simple explanation...

...or perhaps there's not.

Do visit me again on page 88. There's always something to buy...in *Harry Herring's Antique Shop of Mystery.*

TONY PARSEHOLE

I'd take a bullet for these Olympic heroes

HEROES. There's no other word for them. Lionhearts, victors, champions, luminaries, paragons and demigods. These are some other words for the brave boys - and girls, let us not forget the girls - who brought back a mountain of gold from the Beijing games. That mountain of gold, that shining, lustrous Everest of medals, literally stands as a testament to the heroic deeds that Team GB wrought in the white heat of the Olympic crucible.

Never before have English eyes witnessed such a display of sheer guts, determination, grit, guts and determination as have been put on by our 2008 Olympians. The precious memories of the superhuman feats of our 350 (subs please check actual number) athletes, gymnasts, swimmers, cyclists, runners, sprinters, boxers, weight lifters, jumpers, runners, horseriders and runners will remain fresh in the nation's hearts long after they have been forgotten.

The debt we owe to them can never be repaid.

In fact, I would go further. The sacrifices made by all the soldiers who laid down their lives for their country in the two World Wars are as nothing compared with the deeds of our Beijing heroes. Alongside the glorious deeds of our golden generation - the likes of Rebecca Adlington, Chris Hoy and Ben Ainslie - the so-called fallen heroes of the last century's great conflicts are no more than snivelling cowards. They are shameful stains on our national character and I spit on their graves.

Our gold medallists are the Greatest Britons who have ever sprung from the loins of this green and pleasant land that we call England, and I would happily lay down my life for theirs. Should an assassin, crazed with jealousy, attempt to pick off 400metres lioness-heart Christine Ohuruogu with a head shot, I would joyfully dive into the ballistic path and die in her stead. Nothing would give me greater pleasure.

Should a lowlife vermin who had never achieved any measure of athletic excellence, attempt to behead Sarah, Sarah and Pippa - our Yngling yachters of hearts - with a razor-sharp samurai sword, he'd have to get past me first. Without a second's hesitation, I would push my neck in the way of his lethal blade. And, as the fountain of scarlet blood gushed from my severed jugular, it would arc through the English sky in a red, white and blue tribute to all our Olympic heroes. I wouldn't need to think about it once, let alone twice. Or three times. Certainly not four. Giving up my own life for them would be the least I could do.

Perhaps that makes me a hero. I don't know, it's not for me to say. Who am I to say who is or isn't a hero? Once again, I don't know, it's not for me to say either. But I do know one thing. The selflessness, heroism and sheer, unadulterated courage that I showed when I laid my life down for these great Olympians was as nothing in comparison to the selflessness, heroism and sheer, unadulterated courage that they showed upon that lofty Beijing anvil where their mighty feats were wrought and forged under the red hot hammer of Olympic competition.

Never before since the far-off epoch that was ancient Greece have men there that's 500 words. Invoice enc.

•••••••••••••••••••••••••••••••
NEXT WEEK : *I'd fight a pack of lions to save Lewis Hamilton from being eaten at the zoo*

WIRED FOR SOUND

Cliff Live Knocks 'em Dead on Death Row

POWER TO ALL OUR FRIENDS: Sir Richards kept fans singing when Old Sparky blew a fuse.

CLIFF RICHARD kept an American crowd entertained yesterday when an execution was delayed by an electrical fault.

The veteran rocker, who is visiting the US to promote his latest album, had popped into Folsom Prison in California to witness local murderer Billy-Bob Hurtubuise being put to death in the electric chair. However, a fuse blew when guards threw the switch, bringing proceedings to a halt. Sacramento prison authorities called in an electrician, who estimated that it would take at least half an hour to get the chair working again. The specially-invited audience, made up of the prison governor, state officials, reporters, the families of Hurtubuise's eight victims and twelve selected witnesses including Cliff, were asked to be patient while the repairs were carried out.

TENSE

Prison warder Crimplene Hogg told NBC's Hymen Prepuce what happened next. "The crowd started to get restless. They'd all come to see Hurtubuise die like a dog in Old Sparky, and they didn't like the idea of having to wait around for the main event. The atmosphere in that room

EXECLUSIVE!

was sure getting pretty tense until Cliff got up and started to sing," he said.

PARTICIPLE

"It wasn't long till everyone in the execution chamber was singing along and tapping their toes," he added. "And that included Billy-Bob strapped in the chair. He was hollering louder than anyone else!"

MUNICIPAL

For nearly 40 minutes the ageless star, 68, kept the audience entertained with a medley of his best-loved hits. All-time favourites such as *Summer Holiday*, *Congratulations* and *Living Doll* kept spirits up while the electrician worked to fix the faulty chair. And the unexpected gig proved to be a great success with the audience, prison staff and the condemned prisoner.

OLYMPIC

"Cliff was fantastic," commented Assistant District Attorney Delorean Vanderbilt. "He's got a back catalogue with nearly six decades of hits to choose from, and he kept everyone entertained until the electrician gave the execution the thumbs up. We were all kind of sorry when we had to stop singing and sit down to watch Billy-Bob fry."

ENGAGEMENT

And the Peter Pan of Pop's impromptu singalong proved to be a hard act to follow. "It was a good execution," said Vanderbilt. "Hurtubuise didn't want to die, and the warders had to crank that old generator up four times until his skin burst and his head caught fire. But frankly, after our own private concert from Cliff even that was a bit of an anticlimax."

CON-GRATULATIONS: Condemned man Hurtobuise on his way to be electrocuted yesterday, yesterday.

46

SPOLT BASTARD

BLEEP! BLEEP! BLIDDIP!! BLOOP! PTOO! PTOO! BLIP! B-DING! B-DING! BLEEP!! BIDDLY-BIDDLY!!!

TIMMY... HERE'S YOUR CHOCOLATE FINGERS, MY POPPET...

YAWN!

THEY DIDN'T HAVE ANY OF THE JUMBO PACKETS, SO I GOT YOU TWENTY LARGE PACKETS INSTEAD.

WHAT ARE YOU PLAYING, TIMMY? IT LOOKS VERY EXCITING

BLEEP

TONY HAWK'S PRO-SKATER-3

THAT'S NICE

NICE!?! WHAT'S NICE? THAT I'VE SAT IN FRONT OF THIS SCREEN FOR 20 HOURS SOLID MAKING PRETEND YOUTHS SKATE AROUND AN IMAGINARY CITY...

...WHAT'S NICE ABOUT THAT?

ER

I SHOULD BE OUT DOING IT MYSELF FOR REAL! COME ON

OH, YES... BUT ISN'T IT A LITTLE EXPENSIVE?

NO IT'S NOT

IT'S CHEAPER THAN THIS! THIS COST £35... SKATEBOARDS START FROM JUST £5.99.

2 MINS LATER...

SK8-A-RAMA

I'LL HAVE THAT ONE... NOT THE £5.99 ONE... THE ONE NEXT TO IT

YOU GOT IT, DUDE

QUACK!

NOW I'LL NEED A HELMET, KNEE PADS, ELBOW PADS, WRIST GUARDS, SWEAT BANDS, SHORTS, HAWK SHIRT AND SKATE SHOES...

£100

VISA

SHORTLY... AREN'T YOU GOING TO PLAY ON YOUR SKATEBOARD, TIMMY?

BLEEP! BLEEP!

AS SOON AS MY PIPE COMES, STUPID!

PTOO

PIPE?

DING! DONG!

THAT'LL BE IT NOW. GET THE DOOR, WOMAN

BLEEP! BLIP! BLIDDIP! PIP!

MRS TIMPSON? SIGN HERE, PLEASE

FULCHESTER CONCRETE MOULDINGS L?

SHORTLY...

SHOULDN'T YOU PUT ALL YOUR SAFETY GEAR ON, MY DARLING?

RIGHT... I'M GOING TO DO AN OLLIE NORTH OUT TO A DOUBLE METWIST...

JESUS... YOU KNOW NOTHING ABOUT COOL, WOMAN...

...NOW WATCH!

"WIBBLE! WOBBLE!"

VWOOSH!

SMACK!

CRACK!!

NEXT DAY...

BLEEP!

HOW'S YOUR HEAD, TIMMY MY LOVE? ... AND YOUR BOTTOM?

FINE. NO THANKS TO THAT DEATH TRAP YOU BOUGHT ME

BLOOP! BLEEP!

SORRY

PS4

WHAT ARE YOU PLAYING, TIMMY?... IT LOOKS VERY EXCITING

KELLY SLATER PRO-SURFER 4

THAT'S NICE.

NICE!? WHAT'S NICE? THAT I'VE SAT IN FRONT OF THIS SCREEN FOR 18 HOURS SOLID MAKING VIRTUAL PEOPLE SURF IN CYBER HAWAII?

NEXT DAY...

HAWAIIAN AIRWAYS

ALOHA! WELCOME TO HAWAII

WHICH WAY TO THE BEACH?

IN 1930s Berlin, UNITY MITFORD was part of the Nazis' inner circle, where she was known as Hitler's British girl. It is well documented that a close relationship developed at this time between the Führer and the third youngest of the aristocratic Mitford sisters.

In 1930s Berlin, Unity Mitford was part of the Nazis' inner circle, where she was known as Hitler's British girl. It is well documented that a close relationship developed at this time between the Führer and the third youngest of the aristocratic Mitford sisters.

At the outbreak of World War II, Mitford had no choice but to return to England. Unable to imagine a life without Hitler, she shot herself in the head with a pearl-handled revolver. But she survived this bungled suicide attempt and was flown home to Britain.

Historians say that shortly after her return she was packed off to a maternity hospital in the quiet Oxfordshire village of Wiggington near her home. It was

The Star with the Sinister Se
LIKE FAT
LIKE

here, sometime in 1940, that Unity Mitford gave birth to a baby boy, the son of Adolf Hitler.

There are no records of where the boy went, but it is assumed that he was given up for adoption. Now, 69 years on, we wonder who that boy grew up to be. He could be your next door neighbour, your local butcher, even the headmaster of your children's school.

But an infinitely more chilling thought is that he could be a familiar face from the world of enter-

CLIFF RICHARD

FOR: As anyone who seen chilling footage of the Nuremberg rallies will know, Hitler was able to whip any crowd into a frenzy with his hate-filled speeches. And Cliff showed that he was every bit as charismatic as his possible father when, during a rain-soaked Wimbledon afternoon in 1996, he famously led the Centre Court crowd in a rousing chorus of his hit *Congratulations*.

Like Hitler, the Peter Pan of Pop has also shown a penchant for Aryan-looking women, dating a very short string of blue-eyed blondes including Olivia Newton-John and Sue Barker. And just 20 years after Hitler's jackbooted stormtroopers tore through Europe in their Panzers, Richards did the same, albeit at the wheel of a Routemaster double-decker containing Melvyn Hayes and Una Stubbs.

But perhaps the strongest evidence of Cliff's sinister paternity is that in his 1962 hit of the same name, he vowed to be a bachelor boy until his dying day... a chilling echo of Adolf Hitler, who gave up his bachelor status the same day that he died in his Berlin bunker.

AGAINST: Cliff twice represented the United Kingdom at the Eurovision Song Contest, finishing second and third. Hitler, as a fervent German Nationalist, never represented another country in a televised pop music contest.

And the Führer was also a committed vegetarian, whereas in Cliff's shit 1973 film *Take Me High*, his character Tim Matthews opens a beefburger restaurant in Birmingham.

HITLER GENES RATING: 8 ☸☸☸☸☸☸☸☸

TOM JONES

FOR: According to official records, Tom Jones was born Thomas Woodward. However, some time before 1965 he decided to change his name to the one by which he is better known. This behaviour is eerily reminiscent of a certain Adolf Schickelgruber, who rose to fame under his adopted name of Adolf Hitler.

As young men, Jones and Hitler had dark, brooding looks which proved irresistible to women. When making public appearances, each regularly found himself showered with ladies' underwear.

Both were fond of mountain scenery; Jones, the green hills and valleys of his native Wales; Hitler, the snow-capped vistas of his beloved Austrian Alps.

In 1987, Jones the Voice got to number 2 in the charts with his record *A Boy From Nowhere*. Was that song's cryptic title a veiled reference to Tom's mysterious origins as the son of the Nazi leader?

AGAINST: Adolf Hitler was a well-known dog lover, and was often photographed petting his giant alsatians, Rudolf and Hans. Tom Jones however, has a morbid fear of dogs after being bitten on the lip by his uncle Richard's Yorkshire terrier in 1947, during a family caravan holiday in Barry Island. This aversion to man's best friend is a clear indication that the swivel-hipped Welsh vocalist may not share the Führer's DNA after all.

Also, from newsreel footage, it is clear that Hitler spoke in a strong German accent, whilst Jones sings in a Californian accent and speaks with a Welsh lilt when he remembers to.

HITLER GENES RATING: 7 ☸☸☸☸☸☸☸

JIMMY TARBUCK

FOR: "Winner Takes All" was the evil philosophy behind Hitler's dastardly plan to take over the world. In a chilling echo, it was also the title that chirpy scouser Tarbuck chose for his 1970s betting-based ITV quiz show. Was this a tip of the hat to his long-lost genocidal father?

Before he founded the Nazi party, it is well documented that Hitler earned a living as a house decorator. According to Tarbuck's former neighbours, early in his career the gap-toothed comic decided to paint his own Merseyside flat in order to save money. By all accounts, he made quite a good job of it. Is this merely a coincidence? Or is it damning evidence that the Führer's painting genes had been passed on to his long lost lovechild from Liverpool?

AGAINST: Tarbuck is rarely off our television screens, where he delivers an endless stream of sidesplitting wisecracks. How different from Adolf Hitler, who was renowned for his lack of a sense of humour. Hitler's speeches, delivered to the massed ranks of his brown-shirted stormtroopers, contained no gags about his mother-in-law, how poor he used to be or the Irish, and were greeted with deafening shouts of "Seig Heil!", not gales of helpless laughter.

The Führer also rarely addressed his followers whilst standing with his thumbs tucked in his waistcoat pockets. Instead, he preferred to keep his right hand raised in a Nazi salute and the first two fingers of his left hand held horizontally across his top lip.

HITLER GENES RATING: 4 ☸☸☸☸

PETER STRINGFELLOW

FOR: At first glance, the megalomaniacal despot and the thong-wearing nightclub entrepreneur would seem to have little in common. But on closer inspection, sinister similarities between the two begin to emerge. Both have comedy haircuts and you wouldn't want either of them to go out with your daughter.

And the similarities don't stop there. Like his infamous possible dad, 67-year-old Stringfellow travels everywhere in a top-of-the-range Mercedes. The ageless lapdancing club proprietor also claims to have slept with 3000 different women. Hitler, likewise, caused many people to suffer unimaginably dreadful fates.

History repeats itself in other ways too. On July 20th 1944, Hitler narrowly escaped an assassination attempt in his Berlin bunker when a briefcase bomb exploded beneath his desk. And things also regularly go off under the tables at Stringfellow's clubs in London and Paris.

In yet another inexplicable coincidence, rumours are rife that, like the Nazi leader before him, Peter has only got one ball after suffering a bizarre vending machine accident in the foyer of the Albert Hall.

AGAINST: Hitler and Stringfellow's tastes in entertainment are perhaps too different for them to be father and son. Whilst the Führer enjoyed a night at the opera, watching statuesque sopranos in Viking hats belting out Wagner's *Ring* cycle at the tops of their voices, Peter likes nothing more than sipping champagne to a soundtrack of Donna Summer records whilst a nude 19-year-old with plastic tits rubs her fanny up and down a scaffolding pole.

HITLER GENES RATING: 6.8 ☸☸☸☸☸☸☸

...cret... We Name Hitler's Baby

...IERLAND...
...SON

HEIR HITLER: Which celebrity is the spawn of the Führer and Unity Mitford?

...tainment. It is a frightening fact that we could be welcoming the evil architect of the Holocaust's son into our homes every night.

So which one is it?

It is only by deciding which star is Hitler's son that we can prevent his atrocities from being repeated, so it's time to decide once and for all who it is. Here, we weigh up the evidence for and against a host of well-known celebrities, all of whom were born in 1940, before finally naming the guilty Nazi party...

STAN BOARDMAN

FOR: The curly-haired scally stand-up famously joked that he didn't like the "Jairmans" because the "Fokkers" had bombed his local chip shop during the war. Boardman repeated this on television thousands of times during the 1970s and 80s, so many times in fact that it begins to look suspiciously like a case of protesting too much. What better way could thero bo of hiding his real Nazi ancestry than by pretending to bear a grudge against the entire German race?

Take away Boardman's trademark bubble perm and brush his naturally straight hair sideways across his forehead, and the scouse laughter-maker begins to look much more like Adolf Hitler. Add a toothbrush moustache and the resemblance increases noticeably. It could be argued that only the true bastard spawn of Hitler would go to the extreme lengths of changing his hair and not growing a Hitler moustache in order to disguise his true genetic inheritance.

AGAINST: Boardman's professional comedy career began when he worked as a holiday camp redcoat. If he really was Hitler's heir, he would surely have insisted on wearing a brown shirt instead.

But perhaps the most compelling argument against Boardman being Hitler's child is this: even at the height of the Blitz, it seems unlikely that the Führer would have given the order to bomb his own son's local chip shop.

HITLER GENES RATING: 4

MELVYN BRAGG

FOR: According to official records, the adenoidal *South Bank Show* presenter was born in Wigton, Cumbria in 1940. We already know that Unity Mitford gave birth to Hitler's baby in WiggINGton, Oxfordshire in that year. Is it possible that the birth certificate was conveniently altered with Tippex to put any Nazi hunters off the scent?

As host of the *South Bank Show*, Bragg has a great love of the arts, which is a trait he shares with his potential father. When the German government launched its own television service in 1936, one of the first shows transmitted a Sunday night arts magazine *Das Sudetenbank Geschowenschaft* ... presented by Adolf Hitler Then as now, nobody watched it because it was a load of pretentious wank.

And the suspicious similarities don't end there. The German leader was known to have a penchant for urinating on women in order to obtain sexual fulfillment. Who is to say that Melvyn Bragg has not inherited this vile perversion? In over 30 years of writing historical novels, travel books and screenplays - as well as broadcasting about theatre, music, literature and the visual arts - he has not once denied weeing on Lady Bragg to attain orgasms.

AGAINST: When Bragg was offered a peerage, he reluctantly accepted the honour so that he could change the House of Lords and the outmoded system of privilege it represented from within. Hitler, on the other hand, opted to attempt to change them from the outside by carpet bombing Parliament with thousands of tons of explosives in 1941.

Another point that counts against Bragg being the Führer's son is his bohemian bouffant hair-do, which is a far cry from Herr Hitler's orderly diagonal fringe. And if Bragg is the fruit of Hitler's loin, he has not inherited his late father's taste in neckties, preferring as he does a huge 70s footballer-style knot as opposed to the Führer's neat, restrained version.

HITLER GENES RATING: 7

JEFFREY ARCHER

FOR: There is strong evidence to support the theory that disgraced peer Jeffrey Archer is the long-lost son of Adolf Hitler. In many ways, Archer's life has been a carbon copy of the Nazi leader's. Both were puny children who grew up to be members of right wing parties - Hitler was architect of the Third Reich, an empire he envisaged lasting a thousand years, whilst Archer was Conservative MP for Louth from 1969 to 1974. Both spent their youth in uniform - Hitler in the German army, Archer as a trainee beat constable in the Metropolitan Police.

Both were sent to prison. Hitler was sentenced to 5 years for high treason when, in 1923 as head of the National Socialist Party, he launched a coup in an attempt to depose the German Government. Archer served 4 years for perjury after he lied in court whilst suing a newspaper that had accused him of having sex with a prostitute. Which he had.

Both men used their time behind bars to write books; the bile-filled anti-Semitic ramblings of *Mein Kampf* in Hitler's case, and the shit-filled self-pitying ramblings of *A Prison Diary* in Archer's.

AGAINST: The only evidence that points to Archer being anything other than Hitler's son is his own denial. Indeed it is certain that Archer, a convicted perjurer, would doubtless swear in a court of law that he was NOT the offspring of the 20th century's most evil dictator.

HITLER GENES RATING: 10

WHO'S HERR HITLER'S HEIR?

ANY ONE OF these stars born in 1940 could have turned out to be the bastard son of of the world's most evil dictator. But after forensically sifting through the evidence, there is only one suspect who ticks all the boxes.

It seems clear that in 1940, after falling pregnant to the German dictator, Unity Mitford returned to England and secretly gave birth to **JEFFREY HOWARD ARCHER**, the future Baron Archer of Weston-super-Mare.

Nobody knows what the world would be like if Archer's evil father had survived the Second World War. But one thing is for certain...

If the Führer HAD lived to see how young Jeffrey Hitler turned out, he would be ashamed of the way he had brought disgrace on his family name.

Letterbocks

Viz Comic PO Box 656 North Shields NE30 4XX

ST★R LETTER

What is it with vegetarians and their veggie sausages and burgers? I'm a meat eater, but I don't go around making carrots and sprouts out of beef.

Frank Bottomley
Bottom Hill

THE youth of today! Saying **NO** to drugs. Where are their Ps and Qs? When I was young I would have said no **THANK YOU**.

Michael, e-mail

ALL we hear in the news is how high street prices are forever increasing due to inflation. Not in my local Poundland they're not. Not a single price rise in five years.

Tony, e-mail

TO God TV presenter Rory Alec. Easter is the time we celebrate the *resurrection* of Jesus, not his *birth*. You were thinking about Christmas.

J Plywood, Harpenden

THE man next to me on the train had his hair cut last night. He left the top long, and shortened the side burns. He was also considering whether or not to have a chicken pie for his dinner. No, I didn't find it interesting either, but thanks to the inventor of mobile phones I had to listen to it anyway. What a great idea they were.

T Balustrade, e-mail

I RECENTLY went paintballing in Centre Parcs in Sherwood Forest and found it a really exciting experience. It made me think what an horrific time our troops must be having in Iraq and Afghanistan. Hiding behind a small wooden stockade, not knowing when I was going to get hit by a small pellet of paint was quite unnerving, and brought home to me what it must be like to be in a war zone. Hats off to our brave troops.

V Brockie, Hertfordshire

PEOPLE think Stephen Hawking is so clever, but when you ask him a question and he is typing in the answer on his little screen, how do we know he isn't just looking up the answer on the Internet?

DNC, London

ON the subject of Stephen Hawking, why does he still speak like a 1950s B-Movie robot? My local taxi firm's automated booking service achieves a passable Scottish accent, and they haven't contributed anything to the field of theoretical physics.

Suavo McBravo, e-mail

MY heart goes out to Alan Sugar. The poor bastard advertises for an exclusive job in his company, and all that show up for the interveiw are a bunch of twats.

Milky Teet, e-mail

YESTERDAY in Brick Lane I walked past two of the Arctic Monkeys. Depsite having bought both their albums and seen them in concert, I was saddened by the fact that they didn't so much as acknowledge me. It's such a shame when success spoils young minds.

Matt Mangan, e-mail

I HAD a wank over my ex-girlfriend last night. I know it's wrong, but I've got a spare key and she's a heavy sleeper.

R J Natterjack, e-mail

Viz HEALTH Ask Mrs Parker the Viz GP's Receptionist

Dear Mrs Parker,
I've been having dizzy spells for a few weeks. I put it down to over-tiredness at first, but it's been getting worse and now I've started getting terrible headaches at the same time. Does the Viz GP have any idea what it might be?

R Sinclair, Croydon

Mrs Parker says...
The Viz GP is very busy at the moment. He couldn't possibly look at your letter this week. There's a chance he might be able to squeeze it in next Monday, but you'll have to write again on Friday.

Dear Mrs Parker,
I'm a non-smoker and I've had a cough for a month now. I just can't seem to shift it. It's worse in the mornings and for the past few days I've been bringing up blood. Is it possible to get the Viz GP to answer my letter today?

G Sprake, Leicester

Mrs Parker says...
There's no way the Viz GP can read your letter today. The earliest he could read it is two weeks on Wednesday at 4.25. If it's an emergency, you could always write to the Viz A & E department on the next page.

Dear Mrs Parker,
I've found a lump in a rather sensitive area and I'm very worried about it. Could a male Viz GP read my letter as soon as possible?

B Possiter, London

Mrs Parker's answer service says...
The Viz GP's receptionist is on her lunch at the moment. Please write back between 2.00 and 4.30.

Do **YOU** need advice from the Viz GP? See if you can get past his receptionist, Mrs. Parker at The Viz GP Surgery, Viz Comic, PO Box 656, North Shields, NE30 4XX.

ETHELRED the UNREADY

ENGLAND, IN THE ELEVENTH CENTURY

MY LORD ARCHBISHOP, A DANISH FLEET IS THREATENING THE SUSSEX COAST

WHERE IS KING ETHELRED? HE MUST LEAD AN ARMY FORTHWITH TO DEFEND ENGLAND FROM INVASION.

HIS MAJESTY IS PREPARING FOR BATTLE EVEN AS WE SPEAK

I WILL FETCH HIM HENCE.

WHAT?! I TOLD YOU TO GET YOUR SHOES ON HALF AN HOUR AGO!

I COULDN'T FIND MY OTHER SOCK.

HANG ON, I'LL JUST FINISH THIS GAME ~ I'M ONTO LEVEL FOUR.

BLEEP BLEEP BLEEP

ON a recent flight back from New York, I sat near Anthony Hutton who won *Big Brother 6*, and I can report that he holds his fork like a monkey when he eats. You would have thought that after winning £70,000 five years ago he would have spent some of his money taking lessons on table manners.

T Thorn, Hexham

★ *Have you seen a minor celebrity behaving like a monkey? Perhaps you've seen Kirsty Wark peeling a banana with her feet, or clocked Christopher Dean picking fleas off Jayne Torville's back and eating them. Or maybe you've spotted Bamber Gascoigne standing in his garden masturbating and throwing his turds at passers-by. Write to us at the usual address and let us know. Mark your envelope 'Monkey Business.'*

MY wife loves the Attenborough brothers, David and Richard, but she finds it very difficult to remember which one is the actor and which one is the zoo keeper. So I wrote this poem to help her out. I hope it comes in useful to any *Viz* readers who suffer the same confusion.

> Attenboroughs both are they,
> Brothers each from their first day,
> Very different jobs they do,
> But how to tell quite who is who?
>
> Nature films Sir David makes,
> Of fishes, trouts and bears and snakes,
> Whilst his brother made his mark,
> In films such as Jurassic Park.

M Gripewater, Carlton

WITH reference to the previous letter. My wife has no trouble telling the Attenboroughs apart, but is quite foxed when it comes to the Dimblebys, Sir David and Jonathan. At school we were taught this little song, sung to the tune of *The Grand Old Duke of York*, to help us out. I've never forgotten it.

> Oh, Sir David Dimbleby,
> He's on the BBC,
> When it's Question Time on a Thursday night,
> It is always him you'll see,
>
> But on the radio,
> On the Any Questions? show,
> It's not Da-vid who'll be in charge,
> But his brother, don't you know.

Hector Cretin, London

WITH reference to the above two letters. My wife used to have trouble telling the four McGann brothers, Joe, Paul, Mark and Stephen, apart. However, I solved her problem by pointing out that it didn't matter, as they were all as shit as each other.

K Fielding, Shropshire

Top Tips

PORNOGRAPHERS. When positioning your centrefolds, try to avoid putting the staples directly over the models' genitals. Not only are they what we've paid to see, it also looks somewhat uncomfortable for the young ladies concerned.

Isaac Cox, Liverpool

MUMS. Out of Christmas wrapping paper? Simply convert birthday wrapping paper by adding "Jesus" after "Happy Birthday."

Roll Fizzlebeef, e-mail

KEEP a DVD of Love Actually or Mrs Doubtfire in your medicine cabinet at home. The last five minutes of these films can induce vomiting if toxic substances have accidentally been swallowed.

T Crone, Louth

I USED to be a homosexual until I went for a holiday on the Isle of Man in the late 1980s. Whilst there, I was arrested for being gay and birched at the local police station as a punishment. I was immediately cured and I can honestly say that I have never thought about another man's arse from that day to this. I immediately became 100% straight, and am now happily married with eight children. Thank you, the Isle of Man.

F Demange, Luton

THEY say it's not over till the fat lady sings. A concert by the Mamas and Papas couldn't have lasted long then.

A. Bruce, Preston and Newcastle

SORRY to go back to the subject of God TV again, but last week they were raising money to 'fund their mission', and presenter Rory Alec told how God rewards those who give. One woman, he told us, donated £5 and a week later she received an unexpected cheque for £1100 from a merger of her bank.

MAD MAX

MOTORSPORT SUPREMO Max Mosley's fall from grace after being set up by the News of the World has prompted a full postbag. And it seems that Viz readers are sharply divided as to whether or not his sado-masochistic orgy with 5 hookers was a good thing or bad thing. Here's a selection of the letters we received...

...It is about time the media left Max Mosley alone. He has already suffered enough. That bit on the *News of the World* video where the pro hits him on the arse with a cane looks like it would be really painful.

Morgan Winstanley, Huxtable

...Max Mosley's privacy has been violated by the *News of the World*. It is a disgrace that pictures of him being strapped down and having his wrinkly arse whipped till it bleeds have been splashed all over a national newspaper in this way. Whatever happened to privacy? Nobody should suffer the indignity of having photographs of themselves naked with little man tits, acting out bizarre, sado-masochistic fantasies with a bevy of hookers published for all the world to see, let alone interviews with the prostitutes claiming that he sometimes had difficulty maintaining an erection.

F Jimjams, Glasgow

...Max Mosley is taking legal action against a newspaper for insinuating there was a nazi element to his sex orgy with 5 hookers. Now, I'm not on either side, but I must admit that the sight of a leggy blonde prostitute dressed in a leather coat and Freddy Mercury hat, wearing stockings and suspenders doesn't bring to mind the horrors of Hitler's final solution for me.

Tarquin Hampstead, Leeds

This, according to Alec, was a gift from God to reward her generosity. Well if giving a fiver to God TV is a thing worthy of such reward, why didn't God just send the £1100 directly there instead? He must have absolutely shit accountants.

J Plywood, Harpenden

THERE has been a lot said about nazi sex orgies in the press recently. Although I wouldn't indulge in one myself, my grandad fought the nazis so that people could be free to dress up as one of the people he was fighting in order to engage in sick sex acts with prostitutes.

J Pottersbar, Potters Bar

I AM currently making a TV programme about the history of flight and I can't think how to start it. Maybe a short, grainy, black and white film sequence of flimsy aircraft crashing, or men on roller skates flapping their arms whilst being propelled by rockets would do the trick. What do your readers think?

DNC, London

I WISH Ricky Tomlinson would stop going on about his arse. From the looks of it, it doesn't seem like anything worth bragging about.

Ross, e-mail

THIS morning I read on a can of Special Brew the words: "By appointment to the Danish Royal Court." Now our lot might not be all that savoury, what with bumping off Princesses and being lizards and that, but at least they don't hang around the park shitting themselves and picking fights with imaginary antagonists. Not since Princess Margaret died anyway.

Dr. Jonathan Miller, e-mail

Viz HEALTH

The Viz Accident & Emergency Dept.

Dear Viz A&E,

I'm really sorry, I'm pissed as a fart, and whilst showing off to some girls, I fell off some scaffolding and landed on my wrist. I think it's broken. It's swollen up like a balloon and I can't move my fingers. Could a Viz A&E doctor have a look at it?

B Aspen, Manchester

● *A triage nurse has read your letter to ascertain its urgency. Letters involving head injuries and heart problems are read first. The current waiting time to have your letter read is between 3 and 8 hours. Thank you.*

Dear Viz A&E,

I'm a non-smoker and I've had a cough for a month now. I just can't seem to shift it. It's worse in the mornings and for the past few days I've been bringing up blood. I'm afraid the Viz doctor can't read my letter for a couple of weeks and I'm really worried. Can you help?

G Sprake, Leicester

● *This part of the page is for accidents and emergencies only. For all other illnesses and medical conditions you should write to the Viz GP.*

Have you just fallen and broken a bone? Maybe you've burnt your arm getting something out the oven. Or perhaps you've got massive gripping pains in your chest. Write to: **Viz A&E Dept, Viz Comic, PO Box 656, North Shields, NE30 4XX.**

Drunken bakers

Do you reckon she'd have come in?

I wouldn't —

— if I didn't have to.

That greasy gin's fucked me *right* up...

Gwaak!

Yeah.

It's not great for four ninety-five...

If a customer slipped in that they'd go mad.

Get the sand.

It's empty.

Whisky?

Small one. Except for a little turd...

This is like sand.

The brown grains.

Save some to put in the whisky.

We can make our own drambuie.

If you told me this was drambuie and I didn't know it wasn't...

I'd say I thought it was.

This drambuie is awful...

Where's the sugar gone off the sick?

Must have melted in the juice.

And then set hard.

By rights this should be a bit like toffee.

Nahh...

CRUNCH

Why do I taste gin?

Ugly Scenes Round UK as Fuel Protests Bite

■ By INGLEDEW BOTTERILL

MANY AREAS WERE yesterday facing a second day of shortages, as fuel pumps dried up throughout the country. With many tanker drivers refusing to cross price protest picket lines outside refineries and depots, forecourts throughout the UK reported scenes of panic buying by motorists desperate to fill up before dwindling stocks ran out.

QUEUE

In Leeds, there were scuffles at an Esso garage after customers objected to a driver who had jumped the queue. Meanwhile in Bristol, angry motorists banged on a filling station window after staff locked the door when supplies dried up. And according to local news reports, police were called to a garage in Harpenden where an angry van driver apparently drove through bollards and used bolt cutters to remove the nozzle from a padlocked fuel pump. Government sources appealed for calm as similar scenes were repeated around Britain.

EWE

At a hastily-arranged press conference, fuel minister Malcolm Wicks told reporters: "Although stocks are running perilously low and there is a danger that the country will run out of fuel in the

WON'T GET FUELLED AGAIN: Energy Minister Wicks yesterday

next day or so, there is absolutely no need for panic buying." However, his words did little to quell the fears of motorists, and fresh scenes of disorder were reported around the country just minutes

+++ ROUND THE COUNTRY +++ ROUND THE COUNTRY +++

❶ NOTTINGHAM: A group of bandits wearing long, leather coats and led by a grinning self-employed haulage contractor dressed like General Patton driving a V8-engined jeep chassis, ransacked the Fina garage just next to the Winning Post pub on the Clifton Estate's Farnborough Road.

❷ ABERYSTWYTH: An evil, megalomaniac dwarf sitting in a harness on the back of a simple-minded giant had appropriated the final remaining fuel stocks in West Wales, which he was protecting within a rusty, steel stockaded compound just behind the dunes at Borth.

❸ BIRMINGHAM: A scarecrow-thin sky pirate, piloting a ramshackle leather and canvas microlight, swooped down over the M6 just outside Bournville and forced a petrol tanker onto the hard shoulder by throwing a poisonous snake through the cab window. The pilot's feral child cohorts then took over the controls and ran the driver over with his own vehicle, leaving his crushed body in the road.

❹ LONDON: Mutant motorists, angry at the shortage of fuel, formed a vigilante army in dusty bondage gear, led by a wild-haired woman in fishnet tights, and took over the London Palladium, where they were last night believed to be holding a series of gladiatorial combats to the death on bungee ropes.

❺ SOUTH WALES: Mohawked commuters in steel hockey masks and riding powerful, stripped-down chopper motorcycles, ambushed a picket-busting tanker leaving an oil refinery at Milford Haven. Witnesses reported that one of the bikers, who had sharpened teeth, leapt from his bike and fell between the rear wheels of the truck, but managed to pull himself along the ground between the axles. He eventually crawled up onto the bonnet, kicked in the windscreen and killed the driver with a medieval mace. The driverless tanker then careered out of control, ran down an embankment on the B4325 near Llanstadwell, and jack-knifed. However, the attackers' jubilant celebrations turned to apoplectic rage when they discovered that it was in fact a decoy full of sand.

+++ ROUND THE COUNTRY +++ ROUND THE COUNTRY +++

after the end of his statement.

EYE

In Basingstoke, angry car owners driving a ramshackle convoy of cannibalised ex-army vehicles ram-raided a supermarket filling station, killing the manager with a crossbow before draining remaining supplies of fuel from underground tanks. And on the M78 just outside Glasgow, vigilante taxi drivers in stripped-down pick-up trucks drove other vehicles off the road, maiming and killing drivers with boomerang-sized chrome death-stars, before syphoning petrol from their cars. Witnesses reported that the attacks were orchestrated by a one-eyed man with a Mohican haircut, who was standing on top of a rusty armoured personnel carrier, swinging a chain round his head and whooping.

EMM

At another, even more hastily-arranged press conference, Prime Minister Gordon Brown appealed for calm once again and warned the public not to take the law into their own hands in their search for petrol and diesel. "I urge the British population not to form themselves into marauding, lawless gangs of leather-clad misfits and outlaws, stopping at nothing to get hold of fuel for their fleets of home-made, customised pursuit vehicles," he said, doing that thing with his mouth.

BIG SMILE FOR THE FARMING NEWS, MR GREENGRASS.

BAAAAH! UZZ'VE BEEN AN' GORN AN' BEEN BEADEN, JETHRO... BEADEN FURR THEY FURR'ZT TOIME EVVERRR...

WAALL...GOMMIZZERATIONZ, PAALMER... BUT 'EE'Z GOD TER AADMIDD, 'ER'Z BOODIFUL, BAIN'D 'ER BEEE... PURE GREENGRAAASS FUR A 'UNDRED GENNERATIONZ, 'ER IZZ...

OOH AAR.

OI THINKZ YOO'M'LL 'AAVE TER AGREE THAAT THE BEZZD DOLT WON.

OOH AAR! CREENGRAAZ22, HEH-HEH!

OOH-AAAR! HAAR! HAAR! HAAAR!

WODD'RE YOU'M LAAUGHIN' AT, PAALMER..?

OI THINKZ MOY BOY AGREEZ!

OOH-AAR! OOHAAR! OOH-AAR! ≥SNORT!≤

MOO!

EH!? YAAAAH! GEDDORFF 'ER, YOU'M BRUTE! PAALMER! GEDDIM ORF MOY MARIGOLD..! 'ER'Z IN SEAZZON!!

YAAAH! YAAH! GEDDORFF 'ER, YOU'M DURRRDY BUGGERR!

OOH! AAR! OOH! AAR! OOH! AAR! OOCH! OOOH! OOH! OOH..!

...AAAAAAAAAAAAAAAARRR!
≥DOH!≤

HEH-HEH!

IF YON RAANDY BUGGERR'Z TAINTED MOY MARIGOLD'Z BLOODLOINE, THERE'LL BE 'ELL TER POY, OI TELLZ 'EE!

CAALM DOOWN GREENGRAAASS. JUZZD THINK 'BOWD ID...

...MOY JETHRO...COUNDY JAMPION FOUR YURRZZ RUNNIN'...AN' YOUR'N BOODIFUL CYCLOPS...

AAR.?

THINK ABOWD THEY HYBRIDZ, GREENGRAASS, THEM2'LL 'BE WUURRRLD-BEATERZ, THEM2'LL BE!

OOH AAR! AAAPEN 'EE'Z GOD A POINT THAAR, PAALMER...

OOH AAR! 'EE CAN FERGET THE COUNDY SHOOW... 'ER'Z CHIGGEN VEED... THEY OFFZPPRING'LL TOIKE THE TOP PRROIZE AAT THE NAATIONAL AAGRICULTURAL SHOOW!

HEH HEH

BUT YOU'M KNOWZ THE RULES, GREENGRAAASS...IT BE MOY STUDBEAST AZ 'AZ TUPPED YOUR'N BROOD-MARE...

...AAN' THAAT MEANZ OY GETZ THE PICK OF THE LIDDER..!

9 MONTHS LATER...

GREENGRAASS FAAAAAARM

MAARNIN'.

BE MOY GUEZT.

OOH! A BABY! I LOVE RABIES! MAY I HAVE A LOOK..?

...COOCHY COO! COOCHY ...

CLANG!

GUMM ON, YOUNG 'UN. LET'Z GET 'EE 'OME.

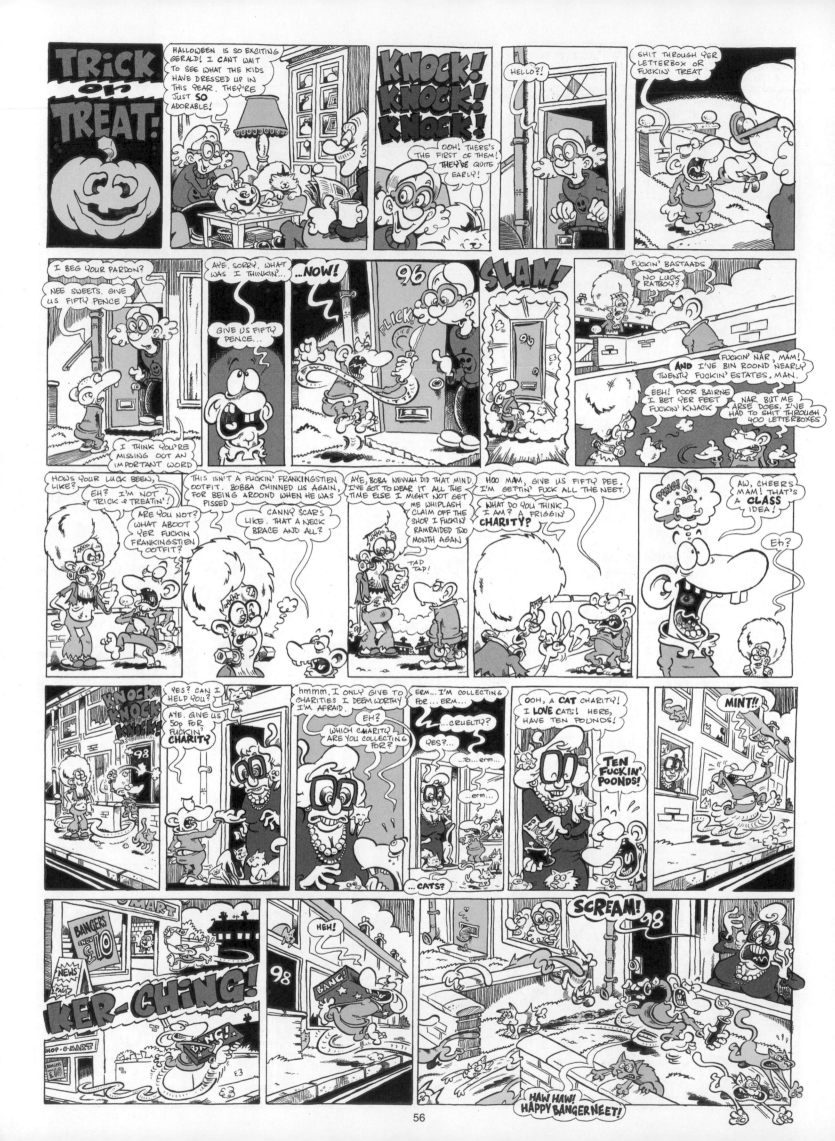

GILBERT RATCHET

SIGH! IT'S NOT EASY REPRESENTING THE LIGHTWEIGHT COMEDY DUO CANNON AND BALL

THEATRICAL AGENT
SPECIAL OFFER

IN FACT, THEIR TALENT IS SO MINISCULE AS TO BE POSITIVELY SUB-ATOMIC

NOBODY WANTS TO BOOK A SHOWBIZ ACT OF SUCH MEAGRE TALENT

OHO! THAT GIVES ME AN IDEA!

SHORTLY

I'VE RIGGED UP THIS LARGE HASBEEN COLLIDER, WHICH WILL SMASH CANNON AND BALL TOGETHER WITH THE FORCE OF TWO BIG SPRINGS

AND SPROING SMASH!

ROCK ON, TOMMY

WHEN THEIR TWO MICROSCOPIC TALENTS IMPACT, THEY WILL RELEASE AN EXPLOSION OF CELEBRITY PIZZAZ WHICH IS 100,000 TIMES BRIGHTER THAN MARILYN MONROE.

BUT OH CRIKEY! MY EXPERIMENT HAS TURNED CANNON AND BALL INTO A BLACK HOLE

THEY HAVE FORMED A SUPER-DENSE MASS WHICH IS SUCKING IN ALL LIGHTS WITH ITS GRAVITATIONAL PULL!

NEARBY. BAD NEWS! SIR LAURENCE OLIVIER IS UNABLE TO PLAY THE ROLE OF HAMLET, ON ACCOUNT OF BEING DEAD SINCE 1989!

P-TOW P-TOW P-TOW P-TOW

Theatre de POSH

HAMLET BY WILLIAM SHAKESPEAR

OH DEAR. WHERE WILL WE FIND A SUFFICIENTLY HEAVYWEIGHT ACTING TALENT TO REPLACE HIM?

HOY! WHAT'S SUCKING ALL THE LIGHTBULBS OUT OF OUR SIGN?

WOW! THAT'S WHAT I CALL A HEAVYWEIGHT TALENT ~ CANNON AND BALL ARE SO HEAVY, THEY'RE APPROACHING INFINITE DENSITY!

TO BE OR NOT TO BE

ROCK ON, TOMMY

WE MUST HIRE THEM TO PLAY THE ROLE OF HAMLET

THANKS GILBERT ~ ACCEPT THIS PLATE OF GIANT SAUSAGES AND MASH, AS A REWARD!

SLOO! THIS IS THE KIND OF "BIG BANG-ERS" I LIKE BEST!

Green Measures Hit UK Bagladies

BRITAIN'S BAGLADIES were last night up in arms after new figures showed that their supply of carriers has reached a record low.

Green measures brought in by high street shops and supermarket chains have seen numbers of disposable plastic bags fall dramatically in recent months. And while the widespread take-up of so-called 'bags for life' by shoppers has been good news for the environment, it has proved a major headache for the country's female vagrants.

carrier

"We bagladies have historically relied on a steady supply of carrier bags to carry our miscellaneous bits of crap around in," said Edna Speight, President of the British Institute of Bagladies and Ciderwomen. "The turnover rate has been traditionally high. Because the handles tend to go after just a few days of being carted round the streets, they need replacing with new bags on a regular basis. Quite simply, thanks to the so-called green initiatives of our

EXCLUSIVE!

shops, old-fashioned carriers are getting harder and harder to source."

Pausing to take a swig from a plastic bottle of White Lightning and shout incoherent abuse at a passer-by, Miss Speight continued: "If the availability of fresh carriers doesn't improve for my members soon, I can foresee a situation in the very near future when this country's precincts, parks and shop doorways will be empty of bagladies."

homing

But Leonard Tripper, spokesman for the Royal Society of Supermarket Managers, was last night adamant that his members would not be bringing back the old style carriers. He told us: "I'm very sympathetic to the plight of the bagladies, but at the end of the day the environment must come

first. Our new bags for life are an important weapon in the fight against global warming. The fact that we can sell them for £1.99 and they last approximately two months before the handles snap and they have to go for landfill is neither here nor there."

Walter

But speaking from her piss-soaked bench in Gloucester Bus Station, Edna Speight dismissed Tripper's environmental claims. "All I've got to say about global warming is 'Bring it On!'," she said. "If, like me, you had to sleep in a cardboard box under the access ramp to the library every night, with six coats on and all newspapers stuck in your tights, you wouldn't mind the global warming being turned up a couple of degrees, I can tell you."

"Have you got ten pence for a cup of tea? Just ten pence, pet. I'm really struggling," she added.

CELEBRITY SWEARS

No. 96 ~ Sooty & Sweep

What's that, Sooty?

He said 'Felch'

■ MY HUSBAND bought me a chair from Ikea, and when he got it home he was disappointed to see that he had to build it himself. It took him a long time and when he was finished he was so exhausted that he needed a little sit down.... in my new chair!

Doreen Erf
Tring

■ ON A RECENT shopping trip to London, my wife and I bought a couple of deck-chairs. We decided to take them back to our hotel on the tube in the middle of the rush hour. The train was packed with commuters and there were no seats available, so we put up our deck chairs near the doors and sat down. I couldn't believe how rude some of the other passengers were, tutting as they pushed past us on and off the train. In the end we were made to feel so uncomfortable that we decided to get off and catch the bus. There, if anything, the other passengers' manners were even worse! That's the last time we go to London.

Hubert Greengauge
Harrogate

Sonny & Chairs
Sonny & Chairs
Sonny & Chairs
Sonny & Chairs
Sonny & Chairs

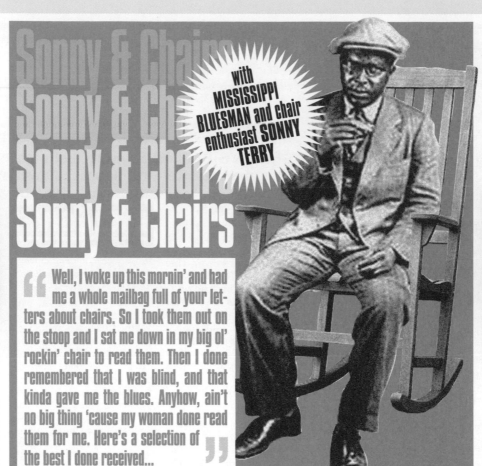

with MISSISSIPPI BLUESMAN and chair enthusiast SONNY TERRY

" Well, I woke up this mornin' and had me a whole mailbag full of your letters about chairs. So I took them out on the stoop and I sat me down in my big ol' rockin' chair to read them. Then I done remembered that I was blind, and that kinda gave me the blues. Anyhow, ain't no big thing 'cause my woman done read them for me. Here's a selection of the best I done received... "

■ I BOUGHT a chair in 1942 and it's been sat on everyday since and it's still going strong. It certainly puts some of these modern chairs to shame!

Les Crayfish
Basingstoke

■ I THINK the problem with television these days is that nobody sits in chairs any more. In my day there was Val Doonican in a rocking chair, Dave Allen on a high stool and Ronnie Corbett in a baggy armchair, and it was proper family entertainment. Now, whenever I turn my set on, it's just foul-mouthed smut from the likes of Ali G, Andrew 'Dice' Clay and Mike Strutter, all standing up and swearing with not a chair in sight.

Edith Scammell
Reakin

■ WITH reference to my earlier letter in which I stated that a chair I bought in 1942 had been sat on every day since. This was slightly misleading, as my wife and I take a week's holiday in the Isle of Wight each year, during which time the chair is not sat on.

Les Crayfish
Basingstoke

■ I WAS very disturbed when I heard my husband, a lifelong campaigner against the death penalty, say, 'I wish they'd bring back the electric chair'. How relieved I was when he explained that the 'they' in question was a firm of local electricians who had taken his orthopaedic vibro-massage chair away to be mended.

Edna Bollocks
Cuntingford

■ SIX MONTHS ago, my husband died whilst sitting in his favourite chair by the fire. I've left it just the way it was the night he passed away on in it, as I've not had the heart to move it. Unfortunately,

■ MY HUSBAND recently came home from the tip with an old, high-backed chair that he had found in one of the skips. I told him that we already had enough junk in the house, but he said he wanted to turn it into a throne. He took it into his shed where he sprayed it gold and spent hours gluing sequins and tinsel on it. I have to admit that, when he'd finished, it did look magnificent. He has put it in pride of place in front of the telly and he won't get out of it even to have his tea. However, I pointed out to him that it would never actually be a throne, as a throne is defined as the ceremonial seat of a king, queen or bishop. How foolish I felt when he reminded me that he was the current Archbishop of Canterbury.

Maureen Williams
Lambeth Palace

Miriam Solves YOUR Chair Problems

Dear Miriam,

AN ARGUMENT over chairs has turned my husband into a monster, and I don't know where to turn.

I am 38 and my husband is 39. We've been happily married for 15 years and have three lovely children. A few months ago we bought a set of tall seats to put around our breakfast bar. Without thinking, I called them bar stools and my husband corrected me, insisting they were chairs as they had a small back. When I continued calling them bar stools, he started shouting and screaming. Then he hit me in the face, knocking me to the ground. It was the first time he'd ever laid a finger on me and I was shocked more than anything.

However, it seems to have opened some sort of floodgate and now he beats me up me all the time. He has broken three of my ribs, knocked out several teeth and I live with constant broken fingers, black eyes and bruises. The other night I woke up to find him standing over the bed, holding a carving knife at my throat. I was petrified. He just gave me a strange smile and walked away.

Now I live in constant fear. I'm too frightened to leave him in case he comes after me. I am terrified that if I go to the authorities, he will turn his anger on our children and hurt them.

Please help me Miriam, as I have no one else to turn to.

H McT
Auchtermuchty

Miriam Says

I'm afraid you are wrong and your husband is right. A stool is a flat-topped, one person seat which doesn't have a back. Any seat with a back, no matter how small it is, must by definition be a chair.

CHAIR ADVICE YOU CAN TRUST	
Wobbly leg on chair	081 811 8055
Chair too low for table	081 811 8055
Wicker perished on Lloyd Loom	081 811 8055
Caster missing from swivel chair	081 811 8055
Husband's chair too soft	081 811 8055
Difficulty erecting recliner	081 811 8055
Vaginal dryness	081 811 8055

he died of a rectal prolapse following a particularly violent and prolonged attack of amoebic dysentery, and consequently the room stinks like a fucking sewer.

Mrs Doreen Mengele, Goole

People With Tertiary Senile Dementia Say the Funniest Things ABOUT CHAIRS!

"I DON'T know where my chair is. Somebody's stolen my chair, somebody's stolen my chair," said my distressed 89-year-old next door neighbour the other day, whilst walking round his front garden in his vest and underpants at 3 in the morning. I had to laugh when I took him back into his house... his chair was in his front room where it always is!

Derek Bastard, Leeds

■ WITH REFERENCE to my previous letters claiming to have sat on a chair everyday since 1942 except for a week's holiday in the Isle of Wight each year. My wife has just pointed out that in 1982 I spent five days in hospital after a penile cyst under my foreskin went septic, during which time she stayed with her sister in Chilcomb. So it wasn't used for those five days either. I would like to apologise to any readers that were misled by my earlier

letters and hope that it doesn't lead them to think any less of my chair.

Les Crayfish, Basingstoke

■ 'I'M IN the chair,' announced my friend one night in our local pub. He meant, of course, that it was his turn to buy a round of drinks. The entire pub erupted in uncontrollable laughter, however, because he was literally 'sitting in a chair' when he said it! It still makes the entire pub erupt in uncontrollable laughter whenever we think about it even now, 38 years later.

Arnold Nottingham, Tring

■ I JUST remembered that whilst we were on holiday in the Isle of Wight in 1978 or 1979, someone broke into the house and stole our television set. It is possible that one or more of the burglars may have sat on my chair whilst they were in the house, although my wife doesn't think they went in the room where the chair was.

Les Crayfish, Basingstoke

■ FURTHER to Mr Crayfish's letter (*above*), I am the

burglar who broke into his house to steal his television set whilst he and his wife were on holiday in 1979. I took his TV, a set of cutlery and several irreplaceable items of sentimental value. I also laid a cable on the rug in front of the fireplace, but I can categorically state that I did not sit on any of his chairs whilst I was in his house. I hope this helps to clear up any confusion as to the admirability (or otherwise) of Mr Crayfish's chair.

T Johnson, Basingstoke

YOU ask, WE answer... ABOUT CHAIRS!

Q. WHAT did circus lion tamers use to ward lions off before chairs were invented?

Martin Lacey, Nottingham

A. IN THE days before chairs, lion tamers are thought to have controlled lions using a small, flat piece of wood about the size of chair seat with four short posts attached to the corners. The lion tamer held onto it using a braced, wooden hoop fixed to the rear of the device.

Three Chairs

■ THREE chairs to the kind young man who helped me pick up five wing-back armchairs when I dropped them on the pavement the other day whilst getting off the bus. He was so nice, making sure I was alright before lifting them back up onto my shoulders and he wouldn't even accept my offer of a reward.

Mrs G Capes
Humberside

* Hip-hip...Chair! Hip-hip... Chair! Hip-hip...Chair!

JOHN LOGIE-BAIRD
HOME-ENTERTAINMENT HI-JINKS WITH THE SCOTTISH INVENTOR (1888-1946)

McEUREKA!

AH'VE CREATED THE DEFINING INVENTION O'THE TWENTIETH CENTURY!

MA INVENTION WILL REVOLUTIONIZE HOME ENTERTAINMENT

IT'S AN ELECTRONIC BOX THAT WILL PUMP **SHITE** INTAE PEOPLE'S LIVING ROOMS ALL DAY AND NIGHT.

SEE, AH JUST SWITCH ON MA TURD-VENDING SET, LIKE SO...

SPLOT!

AND HOOTS PRESTO! IT DEPOSITS AN UNENDING STREAM OF FAECES RIGHT ONTAE YE CARPET! BRILLIANT!

HO HO! MA DEVICE CERTAINLY SEEMS TAE BE A HIT WITH MA FAMILY!

YES DEAR. THE CHILDREN ARE ABSOLUTELY TRANSFIXED BY ITS CEASELESS PRODUCTION OF TURD AFTER TURD.

MAMA MIA! THAT-A MACHINE WILL NEVER CATCH ON, SIGNOR LOGIE-BAIRD!

OCH! IT'S YON ITALIAN INVENTOR GUGLIELMO MARCONI, FRAE NEXT DOOR.

YORRA CONTRAPTION WILL-A NEVER REPLACE MY TRADITIONAL BOLLOCKS-SPOUTING WIRELESS BOX!

FLUMP

SEE-A HOW MY CHILDREN GATHER ROUND TO LISTEN TO DA ENDLESS CASCADE OFFA BOLLOCKS WHICH-A POURS OUT OF IT ALL DAY.

HEY! YOU TWO!

HUNH?

COME AND SEE ALL THE EXCREMENT BEING PUMPED INTO OUR LIVING-ROOM ~ IT'S GREAT!

WOW! WE'LL BE RIGHT OVER!

COOL! THIS IS LOADS BETTER THAN OUR DAD'S BORING OLD BOLLOCKS-SPOUTING MACHINE!

BAH! WE'LL-A SEE ABOUT THAT!

I'LL TIE A STRAND OFFA MY MAMA'S SPECIAL EXTRA-STRONG SPAGHETTI AROUND DA SHIT-PUMPING TUBE

DA HO HO! THAT'LL STOPPA DA TURDS FROM GETTING THROUGH!

DA-A-D! THE SET'S ON THE BLINK ~ ALL THE SHITE IS JUST GOING UP AND DOWN.

McBAH! THE HORIZONTAL HOLD MUST'VE GONE!

I'LL TRY GIVING THE SET A WEE TAP

BOOT!

EH?

O SOLE MIO!

SPLOTCH!

THERE. IT'S WORKING AGAIN THE NOO.

MAMA MIA! I AM-A COVERED IN A PACKED EVENING'S ENTERTAINMENT FORRA ALL THE FAMILY.

NEVER-A MIND ~ I HAVE ANOTHER IDEA.

BARBER

LUIGI'S

ITALIANO HAIR-A RESTORER

I'VE-A BORROWED THIS-A BOTTLE OF HAIR-RESTORER FROM MY UNCLE LUIGI'S BARBER SHOP.

DA SNIGGER!

GLUG

SIGNOR LOGIE-BAIRD'S INVENTION WILL-A BE 'HAIR' TODAY ANNA GONE TOMORROW!

DA-A-D! WE CAN'T SEE THE SHIT PROPERLY ~ IT'S GONE ALL FUZZY

JINGS! IT MUST BE THE RECEPTION.

COME ON ~ WE MAY AS WELL GO NEXT DOOR AND LISTEN TO OUR DAD'S BOLLOCKS-SPOUTING MACHINE.

WHIT COULD'VE MADE THE FAECES GAE ALL FUZZY?

OHO! AN EMPTY BOTTLE O' HAIR RESTORER!

YON PIZZA-MUNCHING DINGBAT FRAE NEXT DOOR IS BEHIND THIS!

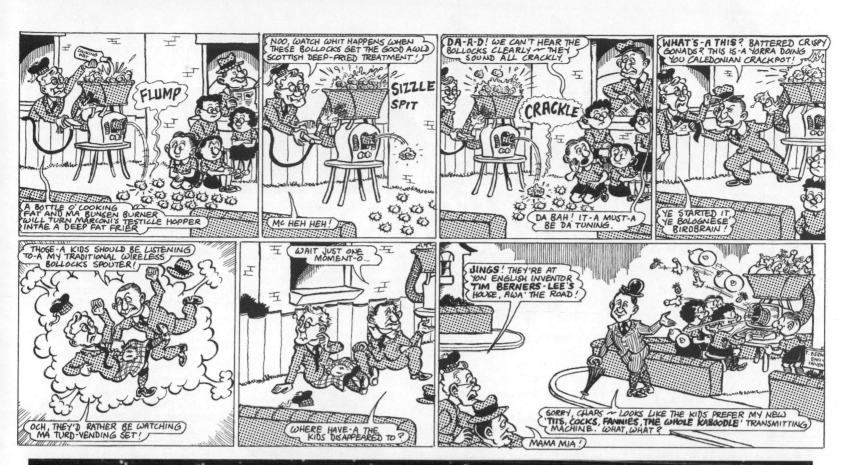

A Big 'Shabba' to the Little Green Men

SHABBA THE TWAT: Fucking awful BBC Radio 6 Music DJ George Lamb and (below) the Caliban probe that will carry his award-winning catchprase into space.

THE SOUND of fucking awful BBC Radio 6 Music DJ GEORGE LAMB shouting the word 'Shabba' and laughing like a fucking cunt for no fucking good reason is to be sent into space on board the new European Space Agency probe 'Caliban' as part of the Search For Extraterrestrial Intelligence.

Previous attempts to contact extraterrestrials by sending binary encodings of the DNA double-helix, Bach sonatas and diagrams of carbon atoms have so far failed to elicit a response. Now scientists fear that they may have vastly overestimated the basic levels of ET intelligence for which they are searching.

'Not every alien is going to be Stephen Hawking,' said ESA controller Professor Etienne Gerbeau. 'We need to tailor our broadcasts to a wider alien demographic.'

FUCKING AWFUL

Mission Director Michael Gideon explained: 'Fucking awful BBC Radio 6 Music DJ George Lamb has a unique appeal to idiots and cretins. One only has to consider how many of his dribbling acolytes used their unexpectedly opposable thumbs to send text votes for George, enabling his braying, oafish drivel to scoop

FUCKINGTWATSCLUSIVE

a prestigious Sony Radio Award. It might make my soul howl in agony to contemplate it, but alien intelligence may have stalled at this sort of disappointing level, and these are the creatures at whom this probe is aimed.'

Caliban's course will take it to the edge of our solar system within ten years, and from there it will use fusion scoop technology to pilot it towards the Horsehead nebula. Scientists say that due to the vast distances involved, we are unlikely to receive the predicted alien 'Shabba' in return for several centuries.

FUCKING AWFUL

Patrick Moore, one of the few people still working in the media with a working knowledge of anything whatsoever, said this delay might be crucial

'We have time on our side,' he explained. 'If you draw a graph with, say, Sir Richard Dimbleby at one end

DJ Lamb to be sent into Space

and fucking awful BBC Radio 6 Music DJ George Lamb at the other, you can see mankind is in an irreversible decline. And this is good news for inter-species communication!'

FUCKING AWFUL

Moore believes that currently, for anyone who can tie their own shoelaces, the thought of talking to an ill-mannered pillock like fucking awful BBC Radio 6 Music DJ George Lamb is almost too much to bear. But if the graph's predictions are correct, by the time the stupid aliens targeted by this probe reply to us, mankind is likely to have degenerated to a sub-animal level, unable to stand upright and communicating by shitting itself.

'It's a shame I won't be here to see the wonderful day. Aliens shouting 'Shabba', humans all covered in shit, in perfect intergalactic harmony. It will be a glorious moment and certainly slightly less embarrassing than George Lamb's fucking awful BBC 6 Music show,' he added.

Letterbocks

letters@viz.co.uk

Viz Comic
PO Box 656
North Shields
NE30 4XX

ST★R LETTER

☐ **HOW COME** dogs get Rolls-Royce arseholes that crimp off perfectly each time, whereas we humans get the Skoda model where you have to use a bit of paper to chase it half-way round your back?

Stevros, e-mail

☐ **ON A RECENT** trip to the Holy Land I was lucky enough to find the Holy Grail - the chalice from which our Lord drank at the Last Supper. I was wondering if any of your readers knew if it was safe to put in the dishwasher.

Alan Heath, e-mail

☐ **HOW RIDICULOUS** it is flying the flag over Buckingham Palace when the Queen is at home. When it's not flying it's obvious the place is empty and an invitation to burglars.

T Hennesey, Luton

☐ **THEY SAY** that a dog is for life. But it's not, it's only for a dog's life, which is only about 15 years. Less if you have it put down.

P Grummet, Nottingham

☐ **I WAS** in a book shop this week and I saw a book called *The Bible for Dummies*. Now correct me if I'm wrong, but is that gap in the market not already sufficiently filled by the real Bible?

Morgan Christmas, London

☐ **THERE'S A** cab firm near me called Tudor Cars. Their sign is written in an Old English calligraphy style font, and the cab office is a mock Tudor building. But the cars they use are modern saloon vehicles. It seems a shame that they didn't follow that arbitrary premise through to its full horse and cart conclusion.

Jackie Paper, Truro

☐ **I WAS IN** the sociology section of a bookshop the other day and next to the 'feminist theory' shelf was a carefully placed rack of *Cosmopolitan* and *Instyle* magazines. How well they know us ladies - always thinking of shoes.

Christina Martin, e-mail

☐ **ACCORDING** to Cherie Blair's newly published memoirs, she and husband Tony conceived their fourth child Leo whilst staying as guests of the Queen at Balmoral Castle. Shame upon the former PM. There he was, enjoying the hospitality of our sovereign and defender of the faith, and all he could think about was getting back to the bedroom to satisfy his base, carnal desires. He is no better than a beast of the field.

Edna Whitehouse, Luton

☐ **SO JOHN** Prescott claimed he was a bulimia sufferer. Well I once saw him in the cafe at Kings Cross railway station stuffing a pork pie into his fat face, and that stayed down, I can tell you.

H Johanson, London

☐ **AT LONDON** Bridge station, the pre-recorded announcements are delivered in a male voice on platforms 1, 5 and 6, and in a female voice on platforms 2, 3 and 4. They are usualy played in tandem and the result sounds something like a 1980s love duet but without music and with more lyrics about security measures.

H Braithwaite, Walthamstowe

☐ **I WALKED** into B&Q the other day and this bloke in an orange and black uniform asked me if I wanted decking. Fortunately, I got the first punch in and that was that. But others may not be as lucky, so be on your guard.

J Tafite, e-mail

☐ **I'D LIKE** to complain abou the rising price of dairy produce, but unfortunately I don't know enough about the subject to formulate a decent argument.

Clatsy Pine, e-mail

☐ **ON A VISIT** to Rome recently, I went to see the Vatican and my breath was taken away by the opulence of the place. Seemingly endless rooms, each filled with more art treasures and gold than the last. I don't think I have ever seen so much wealth accumulated in one place. Then last week, a nun had the nerve to shake a collecting tin under my nose as I came out of Morrison's, the cheeky bitch.

M Franklyn, Newcastle

☐ **WHEN USING** my local bus service, I've noticed that when we approach the bus on the opposite run, the drivers acknowledge each other with a friendly wave. I wonder if airline pilots do the same when involved in mid-air near-miss incidents.

Roger Handrail, Nottingham

☐ **ON MONDAY** 19th May whilst driving down the M69 from Leicester to Coventry, I saw a huge black cloud formation covering most of Warwickshire, that clearly depicted a polar bear on its back receiving oral sex off a buffalo. I was disgusted and shocked to think that there could have been children watching. Have any of your readers seen such sordid sex acts taking place right above our heads in broad daylight?

David Bucknall, e-mail

A WOMAN on TV just confessed her phobia of sharks. I don't think a rational fear of a dangerous predator counts as a phobia.

Melrose Place, Croydon

I REALISE it's not very PC, but how about a picture of a sexy blonde piece moving three golliwogs on a forklift truck?

H Plywood, Hull

* *Do you have any politically incorrect picture requests? Perhaps you'd like to see a black and white minstrel slapping a Miss World on the arse, or a man doing an impression of a gay chinaman with a handbag and a lampshade on his head. Write to us at the usual address.*

ToP TiPs

GOD. Annoy cyclists by making sure that the wind is blowing in their faces whatever direction they cycle in. For added entertainment, make sure the wind is blowing from behind as people leave the hairdressers.

Grant Warner, New Malden

LADIES. Cause unnecessary congestion at petrol forecourts by waiting for the pumps on the side nearest your petrol cap, as the 9-foot long hose may not reach round your 5-foot wide hatchback.

I Keir, e-mail

PRETEND to be a tiny person by pouring all the crisps from a multi-pack bag into the big bag they came in, and eating them out of that.

Alastair Baverstock, e-mail

AIR FRANCE. Avoid paying compensation to passengers whose bags you have lost by simply not replying to any of their letters or e-mails. Chances are it won't be worth their while pursuing you through the courts.

T Bradbury, Winchester

MOTORISTS. Deflate all your tyres before putting 20p in the forecourt airline machine. That way you'll get your money's worth.

Oliver Hardy, e-mail

HOMELESS people. Lighten your load by not buying a dog.

Ryan, e-mail

FOREIGNERS. Improve your English swearword vocabulary by dawdling aimlessly with your friends in front of the entrance to Oxford Circus tube station at 5.30pm every afternoon. Advanced linguists might like to try zig-zagging down the steps at a snail's pace while texting everyone back home.

Mark Glover, Coventry

ToP TiPs

toptips@viz.co.uk

I HAVE JUST subscribed to several adult entertainment channels, including Channel X, Playboy TV and Red Hot Amateurs, and frankly, it's not the kind of thing I expected to see on a family TV set.

M Parker, London

THEY CERTAINLY don't make horses like they used to. In the olden days, cowboys and indians would gallop along shooting each other and whooping. Now when you see a horse you have to practically stop your car and creep past so as you don't frighten them. Bring back the old 'hard' horses, I say.

R Karslake, Oxon

letters@viz.co.uk

FREAKS THESE days are nowhere near as good as they used to be. In Victorian times, they would put them on show and you could throw things at them. You couldn't do that now, oh no. These days they've got rights and everything and you're not even allowed to point at them and laugh.

M Barracuda, Totnes

WHENEVER you choose to define a particularly low-rank porn mag in your cartoons, you always depict *Razzle*. As an editor of low-rank bongo mags, I would like to make a case for *Escort* being the lowest ranking and therefore more deserving of ridicule. Either that or *Swingmag*.

James Hundleby
Editor, Escort & Swingmag

I CAN'T understand all this fuss about 'evil' Josef Fritzl? As I remember the last time an Austrian hid his young lover and seven children from the authorities the story was turned into the most successful and beloved film musical ever. People are so fickle.

Ralfe Inger, e-mail

IF THERE ARE any priests reading this, can I ask a question? It seems that 'Acts of God' usually incorporate awful things like typhoons, and 'Playing God' usually incorporates good things like trying to save people's lives. So how come it's the latter which you are always trying to ban? I personally have a bigger problem with the millions of people your boss kills each year with his haphazard storms.

Christina Martin, e-mail

WHY DO THE children of celebrities assume they are celebrities as well just because their parents are? I'm a carpenter, and if my kids thought they could put up roofing joists just because I can, someone could get hurt. Come on, celebs, get off the drugs and get a grip on your kids.

Dave Copingsaw, e-mail

I WORK AS a Fire Safety Officer at the Cadbury's factory in Bournville, and I am the butt of many a joke in my local, as people remind me that I am "about as much use as a chocolate fireguard." However, I have the last laugh as they fail to realise that I have an unblemished record in over 28 years of service.

C Dexter, Bournville

I DON'T understand all this objection to 'Frankenstein' science, creating animal/human embryos. Environmentalists are forever telling us how many endangered animals are nearing extinction, yet when scientists make a real effort to invent a few new species, people still bloody moan.

Gerry Paton, e-mail

DISCO FIRE SAFETY

Don't.... Burn, Baby Burn ...in a DOMESTIC INFERNO!

DANCE your way to safety with the **SENSATIONAL** Disco Smoke Alarm

HOT! HOT! HOT!

KEEP ON MOVIN'

GET DOWN GET DOWN stairs away from the source of the fire!

Increase your chances of STAYIN' ALIVE in the event of a house fire by fitting a BOOGIESON'S Disco Smoke Alarm!

Affix the eyecatching glitterball smoke detector, choose one of the FUNKY FLOOR-FILLING alarm settings, and sleep soundly.

But when you hear the PULSATING DISCO HIT of your choice, you know things are HOTTIN' UP, so head for a suitable fire exit!

* Please note that in order to create an authentic dancefloor vibe, the Boogieson's Disco Smoke Alarm contains a genuine GT4500 nightclub smoke machine which switches on alongside the alarm sound and light show filling your home with clouds of thick glycol vapour.

Please refer installation to a qualified FUNKI Registered disco fitter.

SMOKE INHALATION KILLS

BOOGIESON Groovin' safely since 1975

65

MICKEY'S MINIATURE GRANDPA

ADVENTURE WAS NEVER FAR AWAY FOR YOUNG MICKEY MARSTON ~ FOR HIS GRANDPA WAS CONVINCED THAT A GYPSY'S CURSE HAD SHRUNK HIM TO A REMARKABLE TWO INCHES IN HEIGHT!

AT THE RAILWAY STATION
WE'RE GOING TO HAVE SUCH FUN TOGETHER AT THE SEASIDE, MICKEY

THIS LOLLY STICK WILL MAKE AN IDEAL MINIATURE SURFBOARD FOR A LITTLE FELLOW LIKE ME. LET'S JUST HOPE I DON'T GET SWALLOWED BY A FISH!

MUM, DOES GRANDPA HAVE TO COME TO THE SEASIDE WITH US? HE FRIGHTENS ME.

DON'T BE SILLY, MICKEY. WE COULDN'T LEAVE GRANDPA ON HIS OWN, COULD WE?

YOU KNOW HOW MUCH YOUR GRANDPA ENJOYS SPENDING TIME WITH YOU. BESIDES, I'M HOPING THE SEA AIR WILL DO HIM GOOD.

AH, HERE COMES OUR TRAIN.

BUT MUM, HE LEAVES LITTLE PATCHES OF WEE WHEN HE SITS DOWN.

SHORTLY
HERE COMES THE GUARD MICKEY ~ BUT THERE'LL BE NO NEED TO BUY A TICKET FOR ME

I'VE BROUGHT SOMETHING THAT'LL ENABLE ME TO TRAVEL FOR FREE!

I'LL DISGUISE MYSELF AS ONE OF YOUR TOY SOLDIERS BY BALANCING THIS WALNUT SHELL 'HELMET' ON MY HEAD AND LYING PERFECTLY STILL ON THE TABLE.

OH, DAD, NO...

WHEN THE GUARD COMES ALONG JUST PRETEND THAT I'M ONE OF YOUR TOYS, MICKEY.

PSST! MAKE IT LOOK REALISTIC, MICKEY ~ START PLAYING WITH ME!

HMM.   CLONK!

AHEM. ONE CHILD, ONE ADULT AND ONE SENIOR CITIZEN TO BRIGHTSEA, PLEASE.

THAT'S FORTY EIGHT POUND.

OOF!   CRASH!

LATER, AT THE SEASIDE
WHOOPEE! LET'S GET CHANGED INTO OUR SWIMMING COSTUMES, MICKEY!

LAST ONE IN THE SEA IS A SISSY!

IS IT NEARLY TIME TO GO HOME YET, MUM?

HM. I NEED TO FIND SOMEWHERE PRIVATE TO GET CHANGED INTO MY SWIMMING COSSIE.

OHO! THAT WINDBREAK GIVES ME AN IDEA.

I'VE BUILT A PINT-SIZED WINDBREAK OUT OF TOOTHPICKS AND CHOCOLATE BAR WRAPPERS

IT'LL PROVIDE ENOUGH PRIVACY FOR SOMEONE OF MY TINY STATURE.

DO YOU MIND, PAL? MY WIFE AND KIDS DON'T WANT TO SEE YOUR BITS WHEN THEY'RE EATING THEIR ICE CREAMS

WELL REALLY! PERHAPS THEY OUGHT TO STOP PEERING OVER MY WINDBREAK!

THERE'S MICKEY OVER BY THE ROCKPOOLS. YOO-HOO! WAIT FOR ME, MICKEY!

I CAN'T RUN VERY FAST ON MY LITTLE LEGS, YOU KNOW!

SHRIEK! THAT CRAB IS TWICE AS BIG AS ME!

IT'S COMING RIGHT FOR ME ~ AND IT COULD CUT ME IN HALF WITH ONE SNIP OF ITS MIGHTY CLAWS!

GASP! I'LL TAKE REFUGE IN THOSE KIDS' SANDCASTLE!

IF I CAN CLAMBER UP ON TO THE RAMPARTS, I SHOULD BE SAFE!

I'LL USE THIS MATCHSTICK AND SHELL AS A SWORD AND SHIELD

PERHAPS I CAN FEND OFF THAT MONSTER UNTIL MICKEY RESCUES ME!

SO! TRAMPLING ON MY KIDS' SANDCASTLE NOW, ARE YOU?

OO-ER!   NOW YOU'RE FOR IT!

THE NEXT DAY
YOU'RE DOING THE RIGHT THING, MRS MARSTON. YOUR FATHER WILL BE MUCH BETTER OFF LIVING HERE AT TWILIGHT'S GLEAMINGS.

TWILIGHT'S GLEAMINGS REST HOME

SNIFF I KNOW SNIFF IT'S JUST THE THOUGHT OF PUTTING DAD IN AN OLD FOLKS' HOME SNIFF

BUT HE'LL BE ABLE TO SOCIALISE WITH OTHER PEOPLE HIS OWN AGE, UNDER THE CONSTANT CARE OF A QUALIFIED NURSE.

DAY ROOM

MRS MARSTON, THIS COULD BE JUST THE RIGHT ENVIRONMENT TO CURE YOUR FATHER OF THESE DELUSIONS HE HAS ABOUT HIS SIZE.

SHRIEK! THE DAY ROOM IS INFESTED WITH TINY INSECTS!

HO HO! BY TYING THESE HAZELNUT SHELLS TO OUR BACKS, WE'VE FOOLED THE NURSE INTO THINKING WE'RE A SWARM OF COCKROACHES!

CLICK CLICK!   CLICK CLICK!   CLICK CLICK!

STAR Gazin'

This week, we take a look at the career of child actor, religious visionary and football pundit **JIMMY HILL**

BORN in Crystal Palace, London on July 22nd 1928, James William Thomas Hill was a prodigiously talented child. Gifted at football, science and the arts, he was equally at home on the sports field, in the laboratory or on the stage.

▶ **JIMMY WAS** used to being in the public eye from an early age. Whilst still a toddler, he had a couple of minor roles in Hollywood musicals, appearing alongside stars such as Gloria Swanson, Marlene Dietrich and Edward G Robinson. But he finally became a household name in 1965 with his Oscar-winning performance as Ulrich, the youngest of the musical von Trapp children in Rodgers and Hammerstein's *The Sound of Music*. However, Hill's singing voice was not deemed good enough by the producers, and his songs were re-recorded by another child. By a strange twist of fate, the soprano chosen to re-dub Jimmy's vocals was an 8-year-old John Motson who, decades later, was to take his place alongside Hill in the BBC commentary box.

▲ **FAST FORWARD** to 1953, when Hill unexpectedly turned his back on showbusiness following a dramatic religious conversion. He later recalled: "I was visited in the night by two angels who handed me a fiery sword. They told me I had to go out into the corrupt, filthy world and preach the word of the Lord in order to prepare humankind for the coming of the end times." Hill travelled to America where, along with 500 of his followers, he set up The Branch Jimmydian Tabernacle Church of the Golden Children of Hill the Prophet in a heavily-fortified compound in the Nevada desert. Following FBI accusations that Hill was stockpiling firearms and evading tax, there was a 10-day siege culminating in a shootout, mass suicide and a huge fire. In the confusion which surrounded the bloodbath, Hill escaped back to Britain where he enrolled on a Physics course at Imperial College, London.

◀ **HILL PROVED** to be a brilliant physicist, excelling in both the theoretical and experimental fields of the science. He spent many years studying the concept of mass, hypothesizing, in what eventually became known as Jimmy Hill's Third Law, that mass, like an electric charge, can simultaneously exist in both positive and negative forms. He also postulated that "...if an external vector force is applied to such a negative point mass, the said mass would move in the opposite direction to the force applied, and therefore the reaction to that applied force is in the same line as the force itself. ie, Contrary to Newton's theories, action and reaction are equal but not opposite." In 1968, his pioneering work was recognised when he was nominated for that year's Nobel Prize. However, although brilliant, his work overturning Newton proved too controversial for the scientific establishment, and so the award that year was given to another scientist for his work on thermoluminescence. By a bizarre twist of fate, the winning scientist was Oxford physicist Dr Tony Gubba, who was later to find fame as one of Jimmy's fellow presenters on *Match of the Day*. Demoralised with the world of science, Hill decided to run away to the circus.

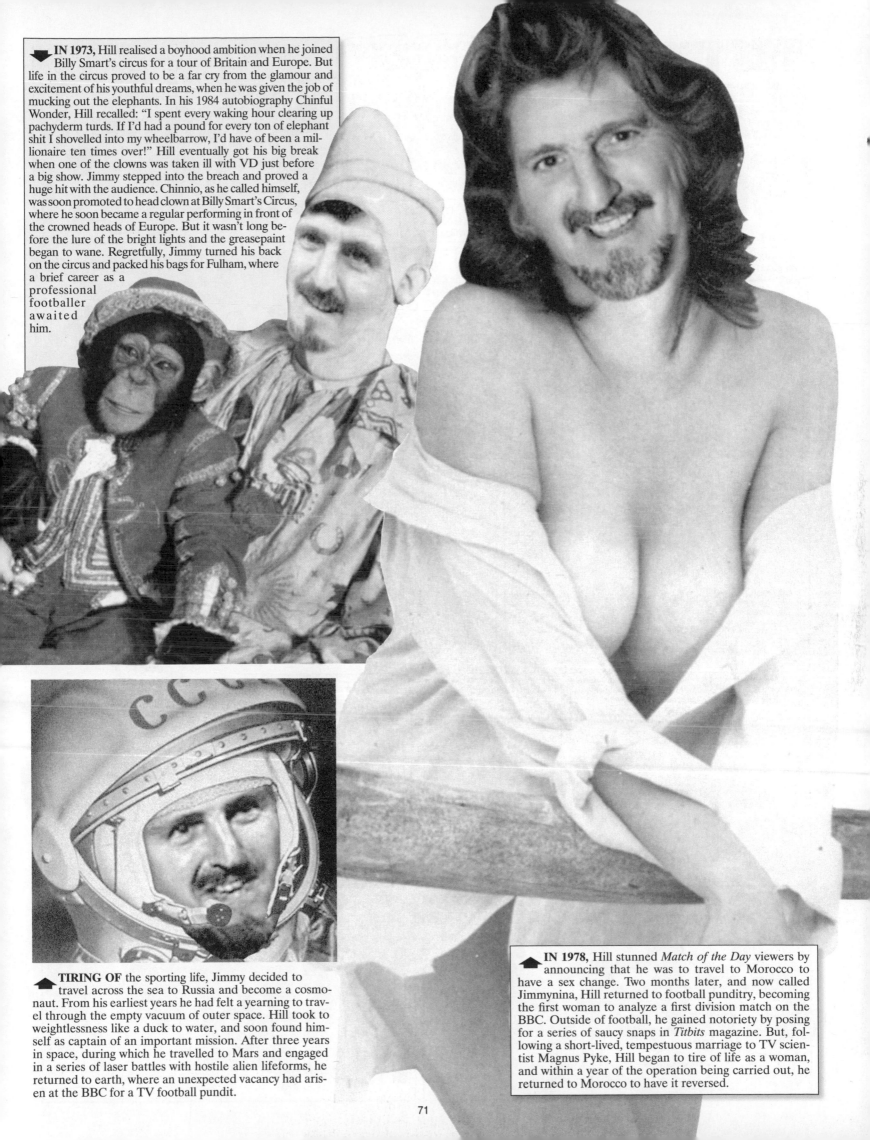

IN 1973, Hill realised a boyhood ambition when he joined Billy Smart's circus for a tour of Britain and Europe. But life in the circus proved to be a far cry from the glamour and excitement of his youthful dreams, when he was given the job of mucking out the elephants. In his 1984 autobiography Chinful Wonder, Hill recalled: "I spent every waking hour clearing up pachyderm turds. If I'd had a pound for every ton of elephant shit I shovelled into my wheelbarrow, I'd have of been a millionaire ten times over!" Hill eventually got his big break when one of the clowns was taken ill with VD just before a big show. Jimmy stepped into the breach and proved a huge hit with the audience. Chinnio, as he called himself, was soon promoted to head clown at Billy Smart's Circus, where he soon became a regular performing in front of the crowned heads of Europe. But it wasn't long before the lure of the bright lights and the greasepaint began to wane. Regretfully, Jimmy turned his back on the circus and packed his bags for Fulham, where a brief career as a professional footballer awaited him.

TIRING OF the sporting life, Jimmy decided to travel across the sea to Russia and become a cosmonaut. From his earliest years he had felt a yearning to travel through the empty vacuum of outer space. Hill took to weightlessness like a duck to water, and soon found himself as captain of an important mission. After three years in space, during which he travelled to Mars and engaged in a series of laser battles with hostile alien lifeforms, he returned to earth, where an unexpected vacancy had arisen at the BBC for a TV football pundit.

IN 1978, Hill stunned *Match of the Day* viewers by announcing that he was to travel to Morocco to have a sex change. Two months later, and now called Jimmynina, Hill returned to football punditry, becoming the first woman to analyze a first division match on the BBC. Outside of football, he gained notoriety by posing for a series of saucy snaps in *Titbits* magazine. But, following a short-lived, tempestuous marriage to TV scientist Magnus Pyke, Hill began to tire of life as a woman, and within a year of the operation being carried out, he returned to Morocco to have it reversed.

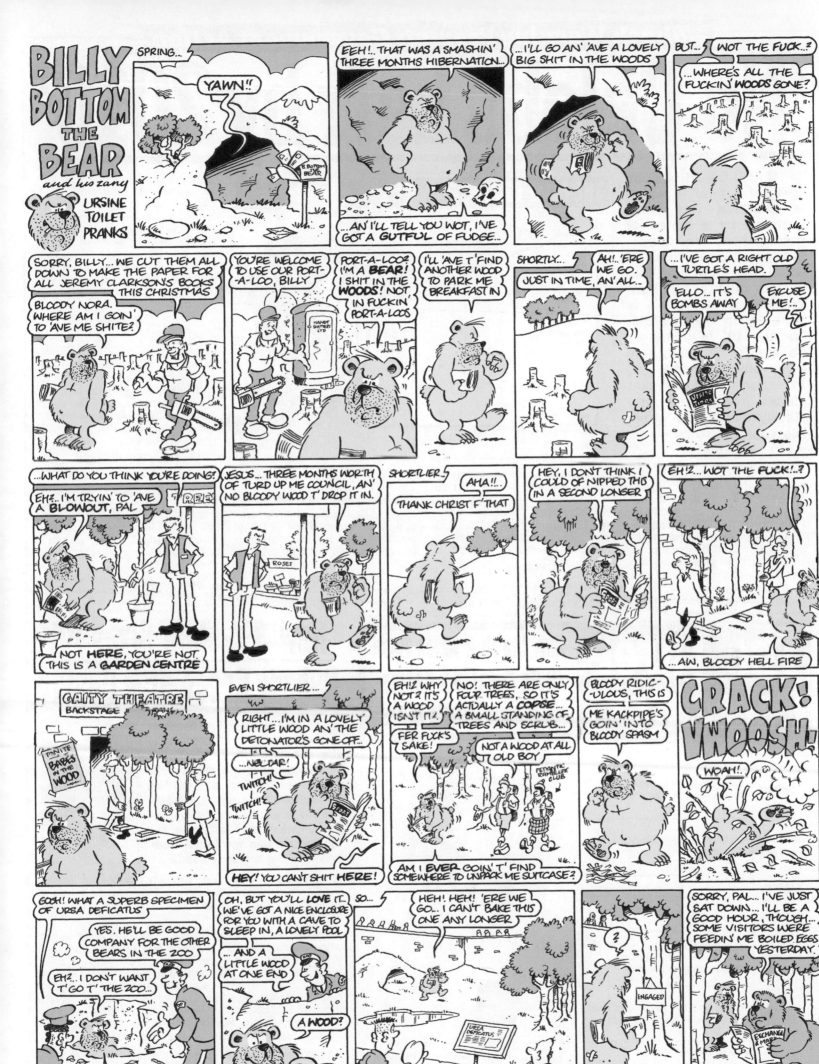

'No Celebs Left by 2010'

HARD ON THE HEELS of a year in which Britain has been battered by a series of natural disasters - floods, bird flu, highish tides at Great Yarmouth and failing to qualify for Euro 2008 - another crisis is looming on the horizon. For the UK is using up its supply of celebrities at an alarming rate, and TV experts fear that star stocks could be completely exhausted within five years.

CELEB-RATE

'BBC and ITV are increasingly having to use chefs, fashion designers, slappers and ex-cricketers in place of real celebrities,' says Professor Tibor Szakacs of Oxford University's Department of Celebrity Studies. 'The media's insatiable appetite for stars to fill programmes such as *I'm a Celebrity, Strictly Come Dancing, Celebrity Big Brother* and *Celebrity Scissorhands* is far outstripping our naturally-occuring supply of genuinely famous people, and the two lines on the graph are going to meet very soon. If something isn't done to curb television's demand for celebrities, star reserves will reach critical levels within the decade.'

LADIES-NIGHT

And the government has been quick to act in response, bringing in emergency powers and dropping the Celebrity Threshold base-rate to an all-time low of 3%. Home Affairs and Media Minister Steve Millerband told us: 'This is good news for those people who are looking to get their foot on the first rung of the celebrity ladder.'

GET DOWN ON-IT

'Thanks to this government's forward-looking reforms, it is no longer necessary to excel in the public eye in order to become famous. Something as simple and unremarkable as being the first evictee on *Big Brother*, being unable to pass your driving test or wanking off Dean Gaffney in a doorway is now quite sufficient to ensure you a place on the celebrity A-List,' he added.

CHER-ISH

Meanwhile the new ultra-low base-rate has been warmly welcomed by celebrity watchers, such as *Heat* magazine editor Boyd Ffucking-Pointless. He told us: 'This is going to make life much easier for those of us who make a living writing about the trivial doings of celebrities.'

TINA TURNER-ISH

'Filling a weekly magazine with news about household names you would recognise in the street can be quite a challenge. With the new 3% rate in place, it's no longer necessary to have heard of someone before according them celebrity status, so filling a hundred pages every seven days with celeb tittle-tattle is going to be a doddle,' he added.

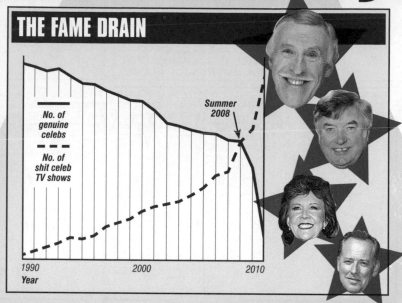

THE FAME DRAIN

— No. of genuine celebs

- - - No. of shit celeb TV shows

Summer 2008

1990   2000   2010
Year

The Three Percenters

How the New Celeb Base Rate Created a Galaxy of Barely Visible Stars

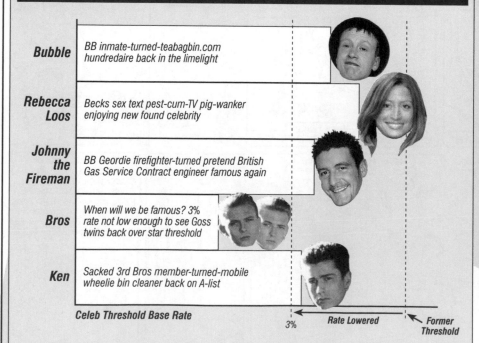

Bubble — BB inmate-turned-teabagbin.com hundredaire back in the limelight

Rebecca Loos — Becks sex text pest-cum-TV pig-wanker enjoying new found celebrity

Johnny the Fireman — BB Geordie firefighter-turned pretend British Gas Service Contract engineer famous again

Bros — When will we be famous? 3% rate not low enough to see Goss twins back over star threshold

Ken — Sacked 3rd Bros member-turned-mobile wheelie bin cleaner back on A-list

Celeb Threshold Base Rate

3%   **Rate Lowered** ← Former Threshold

New 3% Rate Gives BB Nobody Grace Star Quality

WITHIN MINUTES of the Government's announcement of the new celebrity rate, crowds of morons gathered outside the homes of former non-entities throughout the country, desperate for a glimpse of the newly-found glamorous lifestyles of the inhabitants who now found themselves in the celebrity band.

In Luton, Police were called to the house of 2006 Week-4 Big Brother evictee Grace Adams-Short, where hordes of mouth-breathing autograph hunters had gathered in an attempt to meet their new idol.

One fan who was lucky enough to meet Adams-Short when she nipped to the shops to buy a handbag was 17-year-old mother of four Shania Cretis. Cretis, who has an IQ of 63, told reporters: 'She was really friendly and gave me her autograph. I'd never heard of her until this morning, but now she's famous and I want to know all about her. In years to come I'll be able to tell my grandchildren that I met Grace who was on *Brides Unveiled* on Wedding TV and was also the new face of Uncle Ben's Sweet and Sour Sauce..'

'I can't wait to get next week's OK to read her column and see what sort of handbag she bought,' she added, before leaving to go and stalk Kenzie out of Blazin' Squad.

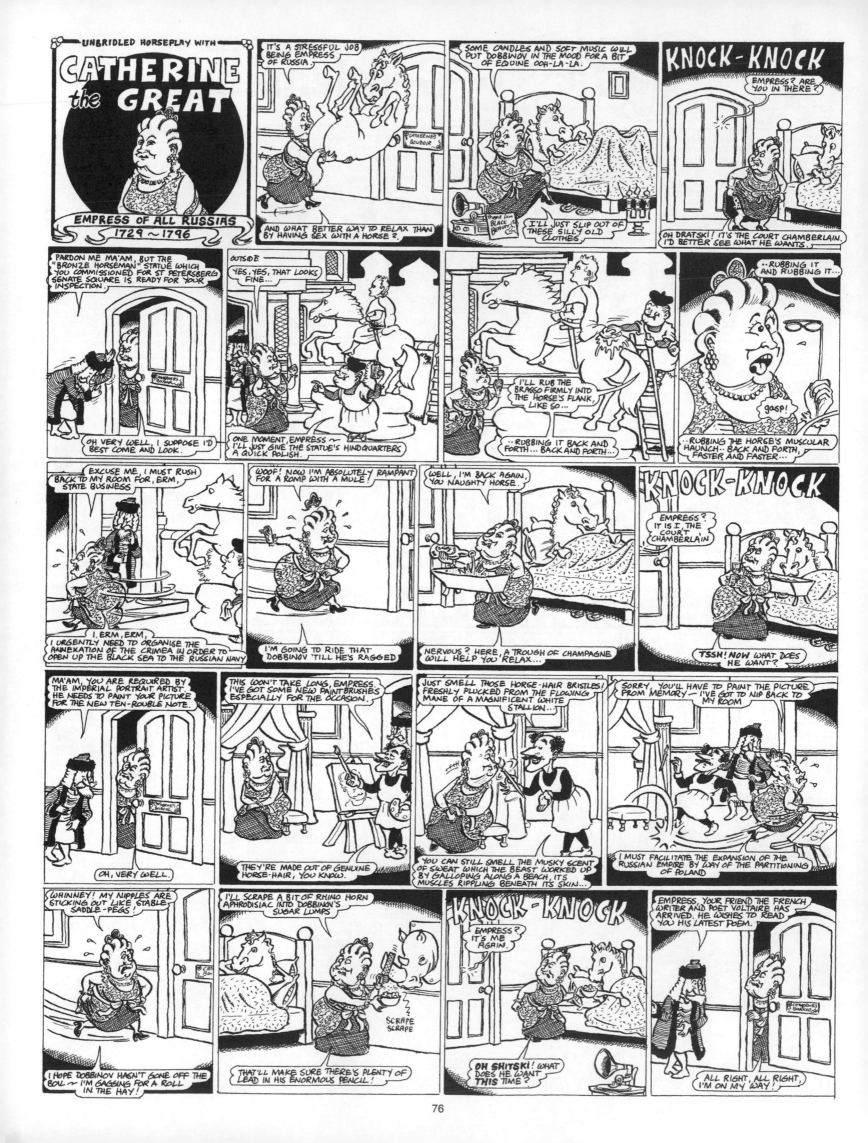

The Wrath of Nature

27th February began like any other for Dr. Charlton Gable, head of the Market Rasen Seismological Institute...

More coffee, dear?

Gosh! No thanks, Glenda, look at the time. I'm going to be late for work...

...but it was to be no ordinary day. For February 27th was...

The Day the Earth Shook

...I've got to go and check the equipment to see if there's been any seismic activity.

Oh, can't you go in late for once?

You've been checking that equipment every morning for 20 years, and there's never been any seismic activity.

How many times do I have to explain this?

There's a huge tectonic fault between Horncastle and Brigg...

Now one day those plates are going to shift, and when that happens, it's going to rattle cups from Kirkby-on-Bain to Thealby.

The devastation doesn't bear thinking about. Pictures askew on walls... TV aerials down... patio furniture upset...who knows, perhaps even the odd chimney pot dislodged.

But Charlton, you know these quakes only strike once every million years...

...what are the chances of it happening in the next half hour..?

Well...

...and it is my birthday, remember?

...just this once, Glenda...

...but it will have to be a quick one.

Great!

Suddenly...

RUMBLE! RUMBLE!

Oh, my God! It's starting!

It's the big one! Quick! Get under the table!...

AAAAAARGH!

It's okay. It's just a lorry going past.

Phew!!

Thank God for that.

Anyway, I'd better get going.

Okay, dear.

Bye, dear.

Goodbye. Have a nice day at the institute.

Oh, and by the way, Could you wash my spare lab coat for tomorrow? This one has all biro marks on the front pocket.

I've done it already. I'm going to hang it out to dry this morning.

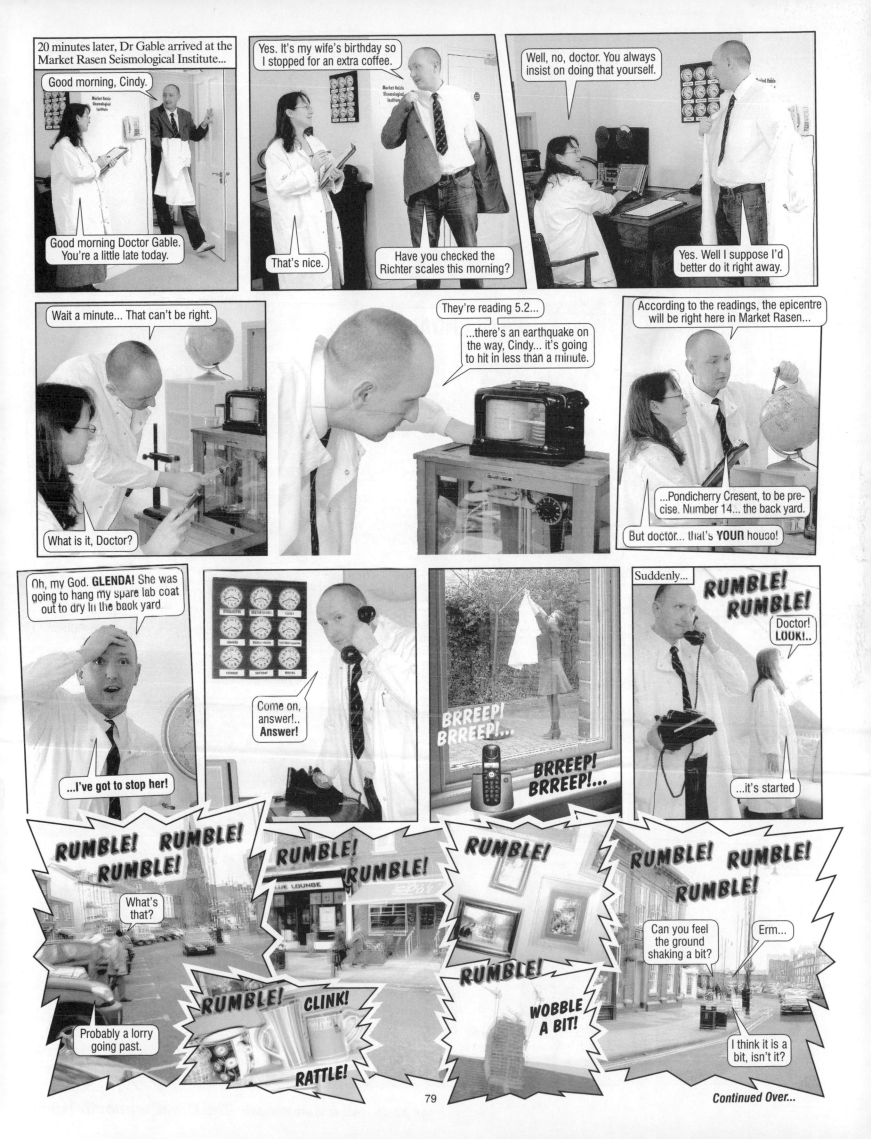

Continued Over...

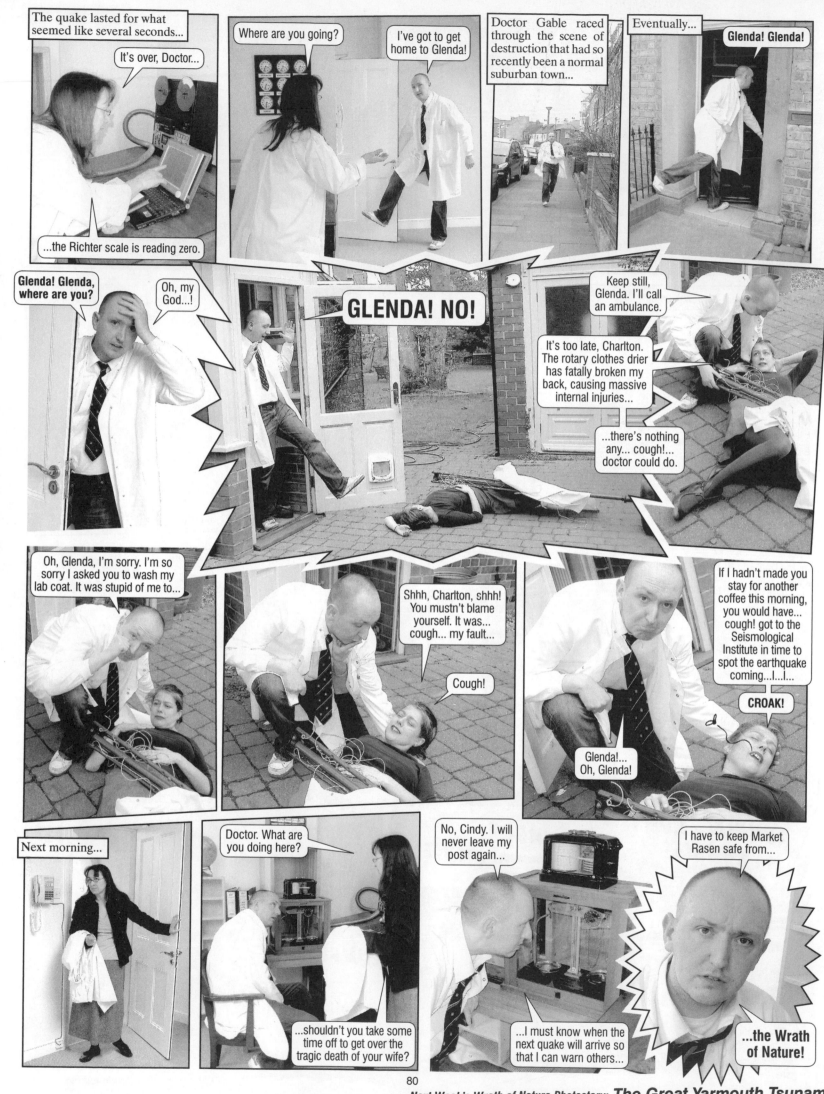

*Next Week's Wrath of Nature Photostory: **The Great Yarmouth Tsunami***

Westwood Hip-Hop Flip-Flops

WHETHER you be chillin' with a hoe in your crib, hangin' tough in the hood with your homies, or attending a barbecue in the back garden of your father's vicarage, you'll be the coolest dude at the drive-by in these smashing FREE Westwood Hip-Hop *Flip-Flops!*

"Yo, chums! I'm Tim Westwood, I'm 51 years old and it makes no SENSE! Check out my flip-flops. They're not just fresh, they're pre-fresh FRESH! All the bad-arsed cats on the Lower East Side are wearin' these blimmin' motherfuckers, from Jay-Z and LL Cool J to PJ and Duncan, and now YOU can walk with the big dogs in your own pair!"

Yo Tim. These Hip-Hop Flip-Flops of yours are really kicking it big stylee!
50 Cents, Queens

Kiss the ring! Damn, these Flip-flops are really comfy! **Snoopy Dog Dog, Long Beach**

I'm giving a big shout out for Tim's splendid shoes!
Dr Dre, Compton

No shit, they be mad fucking straight fo' SURE! 'Zactly!
Mrs Bizzle, straight outta Essex

INSTRUCTIONS

Check you shoe size against the enlargement chart below and blow your flip-flops up by the required amount on a photocopier. Cut out the flip-flops, then get a grown-up to punch the strap-holes through where marked, using a pencil and a block of plasticine. *Bang in your FACE!* Use pipecleaners as shown in the diagram to make the toe-straps, securing them with knots. *Word UP!* Now you're ready to hit the beach, lookin' straight up GANGSTA! *Crack is WACK, you blastin' OFF!*

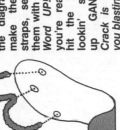

Hip-Hop Flip-Flop Enlargement Chart

Shoe size			enlargement
UK	EU	US	
5	39	6	0%
6	40	5	115%
7	41	8	130%
8	42	9	142%
9	43	8	160%
10	44	11	175%
11	45	15	193%

They da shiznit!

ROGER MELLIE

THE MAN ON THE TELLY

REX WINDARSE PUBLISHING

RECEPTION

HI, THERE, REX. SORRY I'M A TAD LATE

A TWO HOUR AND TWENTY MINUTE TAD TO BE PRECISE, ROGER...

STILL, YOU'RE HERE NOW, SO LETS GET ON WITH THE MEETING.

CUP OF COFFEE PLEASE, LOVE. THREE SUGARS

OKAY, ROGER

I'VE HAD A CHANCE TO GO THROUGH YOUR AUTOBIOGRAPHY... 'JOLLY ROGER - A LIFE ON THE TELLY'

THAT'S GREAT

AND, ERM...

NOW, I WANT HALF A MILLION NON-RETURNABLE ADVANCE UP FRONT, PLUS 20% OF THE COVER PRICE OF EVERY COPY PRINTED...

...THAT'S PRINTED, REX, NOT SHIFTED!

ROGER...

...NO DISCOUNTS FOR BULK, NEITHER. IF TESCO OR ASDA OR THE LIKE START NEGOTIATING THE PRICE DOWN, TELL 'EM TO FUCK OFF, REX.

CHEEKY BASTARDS!

...AND NO SALE OR RETURN, EITHER

...OKAY!?

...NONE!

ROGER...

ROGER...

REX WINDARSE PUBLISHING

I DON'T WANT YOU TURNING UP ON BOXING DAY WANTING HALF YOUR WEDGE BACK BECAUSE BORDERS HAVE GOT A SKIPFULL OF THE FUCKERS LEFT OVER...

...THEY BUY 'EM...THEY'RE BOUGHT!

RIGHT!.. TRANSLATION RIGHTS, TALKING BOOKS, LARGE PRINT, AND BRAILLE EDITIONS... I WANT 60% OF THE...

IF I CAN STOP YOU THERE, ROGER.

...I'M AFRAID WE'RE NOT GOING TO PUBLISH IT IN THAT FORM...

...IT JUST WON'T BE A BIG ENOUGH SELLER.

WHAT!?! WHAT DO YOU MEAN!? IT'S A CELEBRITY BIOGRAPHY, REX...YOU CAN'T MOVE FOR THE FUCKERS IN BOOKSHOPS THIS YEAR...IT'S A SURE FIRE WINNER

EVERYONE IN THE BIZ IS AT IT... RICHARD MADELEY, FERN BRITTON, THAT COMEDIENNE WOMAN...Y'KNOW...THAT...BLOODY FAT VICAR ONE. WOTSERNAME

YES, I KNOW ROGER, BUT...

200 PAGES OF TOP CELEB ANECDOTES, THAT...PLUS 16 PAGES OF PHOTOS OF ME AND BRUCIE PLAYING GOLF...

YES, BUT...

AND LOADS OF ME BEING INTRODUCED TO HER MAJ AT THE ROYAL VARIETY SHOW

BUT THERE'S THE PROBLEM, ROGER

WHAT?

THAT TIRED SHOWBIZ AUTOBIOGRAPHY FORMAT WENT OUT, YEARS AGO...

NOBODY THESE DAYS CARES ABOUT THE LORDS TAVERNERS, OR THE WATER RATS, OR STORIES ABOUT YOU CATCHING TARBY IN TERRY-THOMAS'S DRESSING ROOM.

THE PUBLIC WANT CELEBS MEMOIRS. THESE DAYS.

MEMOIRS?

YOU KNOW...DEPRIVED CHILDHOOD, ALCOHOL AND DRUG ABUSE....

...HOLLOW TRAPPINGS OF SUCCESS, CAREER SETBACKS, NERVOUS BREAKDOWNS... THAT SORT OF THING

I SEE!

DID YOUR DAD EVER BEAT YOU?

FORD'S ESCORTS

DEARBORN MICHIGAN, 1903

BEHOLD, GENTLEMEN – MY **FIRST** **AUTOMOBILE!** BY MAKING TRANSPORT AFFORDABLE TO ALL, THIS MACHINE IS GOING TO **RE-SHAPE** THE **VERY FACE** OF **AMERICA!**

OOOOOH!

YES, SOON MY MOTORCARS WILL FILL EVERY STREET AND HIGHWAY IN THE NATION – USHERING IN A **BRIGHT NEW CENTURY** OF **PROGRESS** AND THE **BOUNDLESS AMERICAN SPIRIT** OF **INNOVATION!**

CHUG CHUG CHUG CHUG

HOORAY FOR HENRY FORD!

HEH HEH! AYE, THIS CAR'LL BE USHERIN' ONE INNOVATION ALL RIGHT...

WHEN I USE IT TO **INVENT KERB CRAWLING!** FWURRR!

CHUG CHUG CHUGCHUG

NOW I'LL JUST USE ME PIONEERING AUTO-MOTIVE GENIUS TO FLASH ME HEADLAMPS AND GET A DIRTY PRO TO FIDDLE WITH MY WILLY... EH?

FLIPPING HELL! THIS EARLY MODEL A'S ONLY GOT ACETYLENE GAS LAMPS – YOU CAN'T FLICK THOSE BUGGERS ON AND OFF!

RIGHT – BACK TO THE DRAWING BOARD!

CHUG CHUG CHUG CHUG

LATER

THERE! THE ELECTRIC LAMPS ON THIS **MODEL T** ARE PERFECTLY DESIGNED FOR SIGNALLING TARTS! NOW WATCH ME EMBODY THE INDOMITABLE DRIVE OF AMERICAN INGENUITY BY FLAGGING A TROLLOP TO MASH ME KNOB!

PUTT PUTT PUTT

FLIK! FLIK!

WAHEY – HERE SHE COMES! AND THANKS TO THE LIMITLESS POWER OF YANKEE IMAGINATION I CAN OBTAIN SOME ANONYMOUS HAND RELIEF BY SIMPLY ROLLING DOWN ME PASSENGER'S SIDE WINDOW SO SHE CAN LEAN ON THE DOOR TO...

AGREE ON A...

PRICE...

DAMMIT DAMMIT DAMMIT DAMMIT **DAMMIT!!!**

PUTT PUTT PUTT PUTT

LATERER

OKAY! I'VE GOT FLASHING HEADLAMPS, DOORS WITH ROLL-DOWN WINDOWS, WIPE-DOWN VINYL SEAT COVERS **AND** A LEDGE FOR A TISSUE BOX – THIS TIME THERE'S **NOTHING** STANDING BETWEEN ME AND A TAWDRY, GUILT-RIDDEN TROUSER-SHUFFLE!

VRRRRR

BEEP! BEEP! BEE-BEEEEP!

WHAT THE –... WAAAH! ME REVOLUTIONARY MANUFACTURING TECHNIQUE OF MASS-PRODUCTION MEANS NOW THERE'S A **HUGE TRAFFIC-JAM** OF **OTHER** KERB-CRAWLING PUNTERS CLOGGING THE ROAD! I'LL **NEVER** GET A SHIFTY TUG-JOB AT THIS RATE!

'ULLO LOVE!

BEEP!

HOW MUCH?

BEEP!

EY OOP DARLING!

BEEEEP!

PSSST!

BEEP!

LATERERER

THERE!

I'VE BUILT FACTORIES ACROSS THE COUNTRY, WITH INDUSTRIAL ASSEMBLY-LINES ENABLING THE PROZZIES TO PROVIDE HUNDREDS OF IDENTICALLY BRIEF AND IMPERSONAL MOMENTS OF SHAME-FILLED SEXUAL RELEASE PER HOUR! NOW EVERY MOTORIST IN THE ENTIRE UNITED STATES CAN GET A FURTIVE STRUMPET-STROKE QUICKLY AND EFFICIENTLY – THANKS TO GOOD OLD CAN-DO U.S. OF A. KNOW-HOW!

BRRRT!

VZZZZ

WHRRRRRRRRRRRRRRRRR ZUGGA ZUGGA ZUGGA RRRRRR K-CHOONK!

FORD ROADSIDE TUGGERY Ltd.

HAND LOTION

AND NOW IT'S **MY TURN** AT **LAST!** IT'S TAKEN YEARS OF DEVELOPMENT AND MILLIONS OF DOLLARS IN CAPITAL INVESTMENT, BUT MY **VISIONARY** ENTREPRENEURIAL INSPIRATION IS **FINALLY** GETTING ME **THIRTY SECONDS** OF **HALF-HEARTED KNUCKLEPLAY!**

YEAH! JOYLESS Y-FRONT FUMBLING **HERE** I COME –... EH?! WHY'VE I STOPPED?

YOU'RE OUT OF PETROL LOVE.

NYAAAAAA!!!!

BEEP! BEEP!

VRRR-RR-POKKITA POKKITA PPHHHTT

OH FOR CHRIST'S SAKE – I MIGHT AS WELL JUST GO HOME TO THE BLOODY WIFE!

SIGHHHH... WHAT WAS I EVEN THINKING?

I HAVE A WOMAN WHO LOVES ME, AND INSTEAD I'M INVENTING WORLD-CHANGING MODES OF CONVEYANCE TO PICK UP PROSTITUTES!

I THINK INSTEAD OF MOTORS IT'S TIME I STARTED WORKING ON MY **MARRIAGE!**

HONEY, I'M HOME! AND FROM NOW ON I SWEAR, I'M **NEVER** LETTING THE **AUTOMOBILE COME BETWEEN US** AGAIN...

HONEY?

THERE YOU GO MISTER CHRYSLER – SEE YOU AGAIN NEXT WEEK.

GOOD DAY TO YOU MRS FORD.

YOU'RE NEXT MR OLDSMOBILE... $10 UP FRONT.

BAXTER BASICS mp

COBLEY'S BANK

EVERYBODY ON THE FLOOR! THIS IS A STICK-UP!

BLAM! CASHIER

SIX MONTHS LATER...

MR BASICS, DO YOU INTEND TO RESIGN NOW THAT YOU HAVE BEEN CONVICTED OF ARMED ROBBERY?

COURT

FIRST OF ALL, LET ME SAY...

...HOW MUCH I REGRET THE EMBARRASSMENT CAUSED TO MY PARTY BY MY FAILURE TO OBSERVE THE CORRECT PROCEDURES WHEN RAISING FUNDS FOR MY DEPUTY LEADERSHIP CAMPAIGN.

WHEN I ROBBED THE BANK, I ACCEPTED THE BAGS OF MONEY ACROSS THE COUNTER IN GOOD FAITH...

I NOW REALISE THAT POINTING A LOADED GUN AT THE CASHIER WAS TECHNICALLY IN BREACH OF ELECTORAL COMMISSION GUIDELINES. HOWEVER, AT THE TIME, DUE TO POOR ADMINISTRATIVE PROCEDURES, I WAS UNAWARE OF THAT.

ARE YOU GOING TO RESIGN?

I MADE A MISTAKE, BUT IT WAS AN INNOCENT MISTAKE. IT IS NOW TIME TO DRAW A LINE UNDER THIS REGRETTABLE EPISODE AND MOVE ON. I WAS ELECTED BY MY CONSTITUENTS TO DO A JOB, AND I OWE IT TO THEM TO RETURN TO MY OFFICIAL DUTIES AS SOON AS IS POSSIBLE.

I FULLY INTEND TO REPRIMAND MY PRIVATE SECRETARY, TO ENSURE THAT THERE CAN BE NO REPEAT OF THESE PROCEDURAL SHORT-COMINGS IN THE FUTURE. THANK-YOU.

IN BAXTER'S OFFICE...

...NOW THIS MUST NEVER HAPPEN AGAIN! YOU'RE PAID £50,000 A YEAR OUT OF THE PUBLIC PURSE, AND THE TAXPAYERS HAVE A RIGHT TO EXPECT A BETTER LEVEL OF SERVICE.

...I'M CONSIDERING WITHOLDING SOME OF YOUR £20,000 EASTER BONUS THIS YEAR.

DADA! DADA! DADADADADA..!

THE BACONS

I'M GANNIN' T'WATCH THE TELLY, ME.

ME FAVOURITE PRUR-GRAMMES ABOOT T'START

HOO BIFFA, WUZ'VE DECIDED THAT YA GANNA GIVE UP TELLY FOR LENT

SUR I'VE SMASHED THE FUCKER, JUST TO KEEP TEMPTATION OOT YA WAY

EH? FUCKIN' ELL!

ALREET FATHA, I'LL MEK A DEAL. I'LL GIVE UP TELLY FOR LENT. IF YEEZ TWOS GIVE UP KICKIN' THE SHITE OOT OF US F'LENT...

...QUID PRUR KWUR

EH? WORRAYA ON ABOOT?

I MEAN, FATHA, THAT I'LL GAN WITHOOT TELLY, IF YEE AN' MUTHA CAN GAN WITHOOT TWATTIN' US, FOR FAWTY DAYS AN' NEETS...

...IF YA RECKON YUZ CAN MANAGE IT.

NEE BOTHA SON! IT'S A FUCKIN' DEAL!

TEN MINUTES LATER

F-FUCKIN' 'ELL, I'M SHAKIN' AN' SWEATIN' HERE. HOWAY BIFFA, LERRUZ TWAT YA IN THE MOOTH WITH A HAMMER, AN I'LL BE ALREET.

NAR, FATHA. Y'VE GOTTA BE STRONG. SEE, I'M DEEIN' CANNY WITHOOT THE TELLY, ME.

F-FATHA, THEZ SPIDERS CRAWLIN' AAL AWA' THE FRIGGIN' WAALS!

NAR MUTHA MAN, YUZ'RE JUST GANNIN' CURLD TORKEY FOR T' KICK WOR BIFFA IN THE KNACKAZ

TSK. LOOK AT THE STATE O' YEEZ TWO. YUZ'VE GOT NEE WILLPOWER. IT'S PATHETIC

I CANNAT STAND T'SEE THE FUCKIN' CLIP O'YA, I'M GANNIN OOTSIDE.

IN THE BACK YARD

THERE'S AN URLD BLACK AN' WHITE PORTABLE TELLY IN THE SHED. HEH HEH!

I'LL GAN AN' WATCH IT FORRA BIT WHILE THEM TWO DAFT CUNTS ARE RATTLIN'.

HOO MUTHA, LOOKS LIKE THE SEASON OF LENT IS AWA'.

GULP!

AYE FATHA. HAPPY FUCKIN' EASTER

THUMP! SMACK! HOOF!

OOYAH! OUCH! FUCKIN' BASTADS!

PUNCH! KICK!

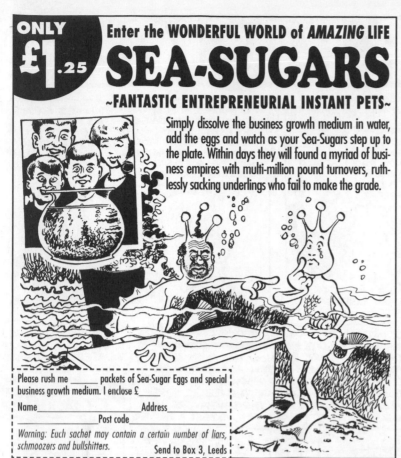
Big Actor Hits Out At Typecasting

■ By Hazelnut Monkbottle

ONE OF Britain's leading film and TV actors last night launched a scathing attack on directors and producers, claiming that he is a victim of typecasting.

Richard Griffiths, best known as Uncle Vernon in the Harry Potter films, hit out at what he called a 'stunning lack of imagination' when it came to casting.

TYPECAST

"For some reason, I seem to have been typecast as a fat, middle aged man," he told a press conference at the launch of his latest film *Fat Grandad*. "Whenever I am offered a part, it always calls on me to be grossly overweight and in my sixties."

CIRCUS

"I'm never seem to be considered to play any other sort of part, such as 20-year-old circus contortionists, jockeys or little girls," he added, before being removed from the stage by several burly firemen using a block and tackle.

CELEBRITY SWEARS
No. 137 ~ Frank Spencer

Cunt syrup.

The Tall Paul & Bandy Barry Fabulous Furry FREAK CHUCKLE BROTHERS

Harry Herring Antiques

Harry Herring's Antique Shop of Mysteries...

Ah! Welcome back. It's nice of you to visit me again...

I see you are admiring this mirror. It's a fine piece, isn't it? You know, I sold a very similar one... 10 years ago to this very day.

A charming couple bought it. But if they could have looked into it and seen the horrific fate that awaited them...

...perhaps they would have bought something different...

We'll take this, please.

Are you sure, madam?...

...only, this mirror has a somewhat sinister history.

You see, it hung in the Berlin bunker of Adolf Hitler.

Every morning, the evil despot would look into that very mirror when he was trimming his little moustache.

Gosh!

And on that fateful day in 1945, as Hitler put a Luger to his head and pulled the trigger, he was looking into that self-same mirror.

Some say that with his final breath, the Nazi Fuhrer cursed the mirror, declaring that anyone who looked at themselves in it in the future would suffer a similar fate.

Good grief!

Hmmmmm!

Pah! I never heard such a load of superstitious claptrap in my life.

Pay the man, Roger.

Yes, Lucy!

Next morning...

Yawn!

Are you still in the bathroom, Lucy?

Lucy!?!

Achtung Liebfraumilch! Vorsprung Durch Technic!

LUCY! NO!

SMASH!

AAARGH!

Roger...wh.. what... what happened!?!

Shhhhh, Lucy!...

It's all over.

Like that dratted mirror, Hitler's curse is broken.

And I'm going to get rid of it once and for all.

Later on that day...

Hey! What's this?

Wow! A mirror! Just what I need for my bathroom. It's a bit smashed...

...but it vill fix up ein treat...

A cursed mirror? Whoever heard of anything so ridiculous?..

But *something* caused Lucy to turn into Hitler and try to shoot herself.

Perhaps it was the mirror after all. Perhaps it was something completely different....

...perhaps we'll never know.

Do visit me again on page 132 in my *Antique Shop of Mystery.*

88

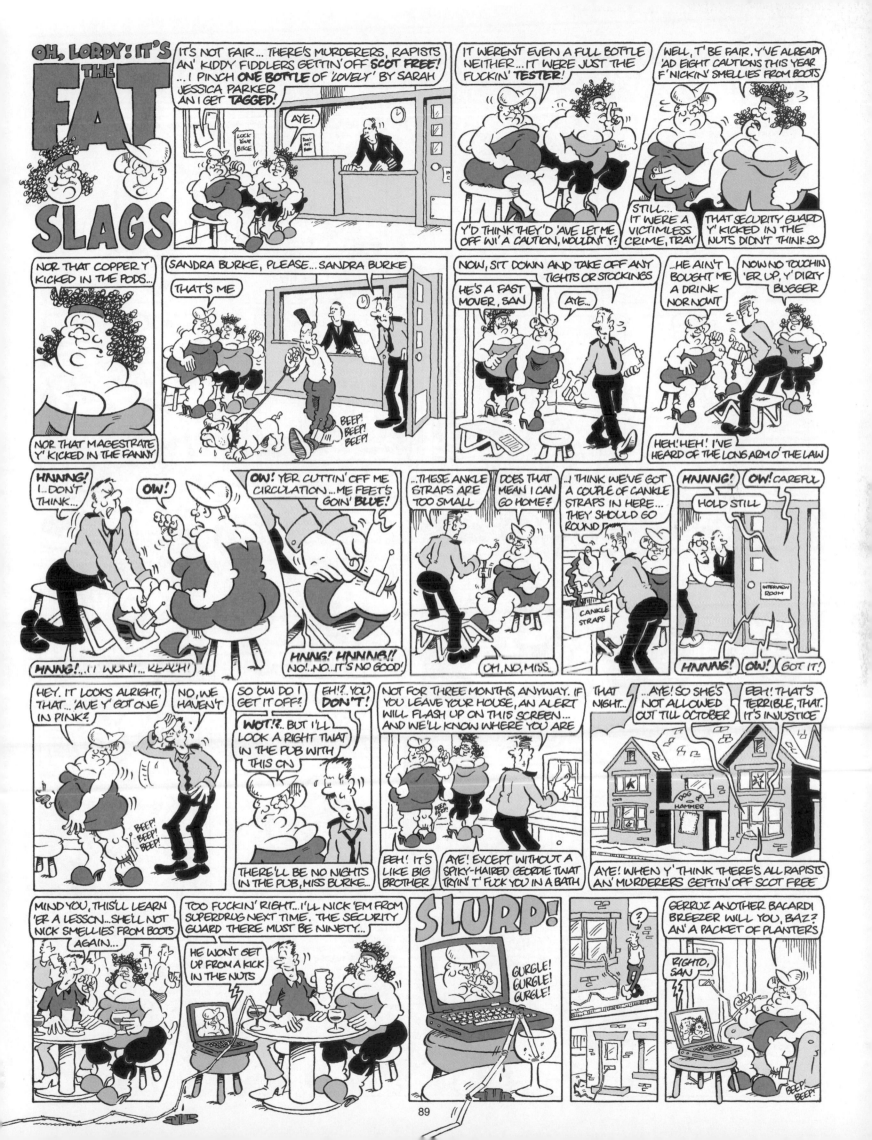

THE ADVENTURES OF RINGO STARR

RIGHT...NOW TO UPDATE ME WEBSITE...!

PEACE AND LOVE. I'M SENDING YOU THIS MESSAGE WITH PEACE AND LOVE...DO **NOT** GIVE ME ANYTHING TO SIGN...I HAVE TOO MUCH TO DO.

I REPEAT...I WILL NOT SIGN ANYTHING...ANYTHING GIVEN TO ME TO SIGN WILL BE **TOSSED!**

PEACE AND LOVE, PEACE AND LOVE...

THERE - THAT'LL SHOW 'EM.

SEVERAL HOURS LATER...

OOH, LOOK AT THE TIME! AND IT'S DOLE DAY..!
...I'D BEST GET DOWN THE NASH!

'ELLO - WHATS THIS..?
PARCEL TO SIGN FOR, MR STARR.
EH!?

DIDN'T YOU SEE MY WEB UPDATE..? I'M NOT SIGNING ANYTHING ANYMORE. ANYTHING GIVEN TO ME TO SIGN GETS **TOSSED.**

TOSS!
SMASH!

PEACE AND LOVE, PEACE AND LOVE...
?

...POM-TI-POM...I'LL GET BY WITH A LITTLE HELP FROM MY FRIENDS...
DOLE OFFICE

...IN AN OC-TO-PUS'S GARDEN...
NEXT!
WAIT HERE

...MR STARR - HAVE YOU DONE ANY WORK - PAID OR UNPAID - SINCE YOU LAST ATTENDED THIS OFFICE?
NOT A STROKE...NOT SINCE 'LET IT BE' IN 1970...

SIGN HERE PLEASE.
PEACE AND LOVE...I'M NOT SIGNING ANYTHING ANY MORE..!
ANYTHING I'M ASKED TO SIGN WILL GET **TOSSED!**

TOSS!

...WHAT AM I GOING TO DO FOR MONEY NOW?
S-K-I-N-T
WOOOOO-OOOOOH! HEY, **RINGO!**

I'VE BEEN LOOKING FOR YOU EVERYWHERE, RINGO!

'ELLO - IT'S **PAUL!** PEACE AND LOVE, MAN, PEACE AND LOVE.
I'VE DECIDED TO GIVE YOU A WRITING CREDIT FOR ALL THE BEATLES SONGS YOU PLAYED THE DRUMS ON.
WOW! JUST IMAGINE... LENNON, McCARTNEY, ...**STARR!** PEACE AND LOVE, PEACE AND LOVE!

HERE'S A CHEQUE FOR £500 MILLION BACK ROYALTIES. ITS YOURS JUST AS SOON AS YOU SIGN THIS NEW CONTRACT.
DIDN'T YOU SEE MY NEW WEBCAST EITHER!? ANYTHING GIVEN TO ME TO SIGN GETS TOSSED!
TOSS!

SHORTLY... ...AH! I'LL JUST NIP IN HERE AND SPEND A PENNY...

GENTS

...NOT THAT I'VE **GOT** A PENNY TO SPEND.

HEY, **WOW!** IT CAN'T REALLY BE **YOU**, CAN IT..?! YOU'RE **RINGO STARR!** I'M YOUR NUMBER ONE FAN, MR STARR!!

PEACE AND LOVE, PEACE AND LOVE.

...COULD I HAVE YOUR AUTOGRAPH, PLEASE? I'M AFRAID I HAVEN'T GOT ANY PAPER ON ME ... BUT YOU COULD SIGN MY **COCK**...

≡ TCHOH ≡ DIDN'T **ANYONE** SEE MY WEB UPDATE?

GENTS

TOSS! TOSS! TOSS! TOSS!

!

RINGSWORTH ARBUTHNOT STARR— YOU HAVE BEEN FOUND GUILTY BY THIS COURT OF AN ACT OF GROSS INDECENCY IN A PUBLIC LAVATORY...

...I ORDER YOU TO DO 100 HOURS' COMMUNITY SERVICE AND TO SIGN THE SEX OFFENDERS REGISTER.

≡ SIGH ≡

CROWN COURT

TOSS!

MAJOR MISUNDERSTANDING

GAY PRIDE

PRIDE

I COULDN'T AGREE WITH YOU MORE. IF WE DON'T TAKE A STAND AGAINST THEM, THEY'LL TRAMPLE ALL OVER US.

THE BRUSSELS BUREAUCRATS ARE DEPENDING ON THE APATHY OF THE BRITISH PUBLIC. THEY THINK WE'LL LIE DOWN WITHOUT A WHIMPER

WELL I'M NOT GOING TO SIT BACK WHILE THEY REPLACE OUR POUND WITH THAT DAMNED TOYTOWN MONEY.

IT'S NOT JUST ABOUT BANKNOTES. IT'S ABOUT BRITISH IDENTITY. IT'S ABOUT HUNDREDS OF YEARS OF PROUD HERITAGE.

SEE THAT? THAT'S HER MAJESTY QUEEN ELIZABETH II, OUR SOVEREIGN MONARCH.

IT IS SHE TO WHOM I OWE MY ALLEGIANCE TO, NOT SOME TINPOT EUROPEAN PENPUSHER

WELL, THEY'RE IN FOR A SHOCK. TOGETHER WE'LL SHOW THEM THAT WE BRITS WON'T GIVE UP WITHOUT A FIGHT.

ALL RIGHT TROOPS FORWARD MARCH!

GAY PRIDE

LETTERBOCKs

Viz Comic
PO Box 656
North Shields
NE30 4XX
letters@viz.co.uk

ST★R LETTER

I CAN'T see what the problem is locking terrorists up for 42 days. When you consider all the death and destruction caused by the 9/11 bombers and their ilk, 42 days seems lenient. If I had my way I'd lock them up for life.

Hampton Doubleday, Hull

* Mr Doubleday's letter wins a ten minute trolley dash round the British Museum.

I AGREE with the writer of the Star Letter *(above)*. I have no problem with the police locking up terrorist suspects for 42 days without charge. But 42 days should mean 42 days. With good behaviour, they'll probably be out in three weeks.

D Steele, Broughton

THE 'Magic Eye' at the Wimbledon Tennis Tournament has revolutionised the game by providing a swift resolution to disputed line calls. Now that it has proved such a success, would it be possible, I wonder, to produce a similar, low-level instrument that could look up the skirts of female tennis players in case any arguments arose as to the colour of their underwear?

Travis Walesby, Rugby

WHAT a shame young Andy Murray once again failed to live up to expectations at Wimbledon. I am writing this letter on the first day of the tournament and he's not been knocked out yet, but I am pretty confident that, as usual, he's not going to get too far.

Mildred Buttons, London

I THINK I must have a guardian angel. I live at the bottom of a hill, and last week a local farmer parked his landrover at the top. The handbrake failed and it came careering down towards my house. I was pegging my washing out in the back garden when I heard the farmer shouting and I saw the car hurtling towards me. I thought I was a goner, but at the last minute, my guardian angel must have taken control of the steering wheel because it took an unexpected left turn and ploughed into my neighbour's house instead, killing her, her husband and their 2 dogs.

Renton Pumice, Cornwall

PEOPLE often complain that television and computer games are stifling children's imaginations and stunting their development, but I beg to differ. As a child, we holidayed in Wales in a cottage with no telly. The only thing we could think to do to stave off boredom was to lift up the manhole cover outside the bathroom and watch our aunt's turds float by when she went to the toilet. That was the reality of making your own entertainment in those days. Anyone who tells you we used to spend endless summer days putting on plays or lying in the meadow reading *Wind in the Willows* is talking out their fucking arse.

Eric Fibreboard, Tring

WHATEVER happened to bird flu? I used to like it when we were scared of bird flu. Now they never mention bird flu any more, and I'm worried in case there's something they're not telling us. Come on government, put my mind at ease and bring back the bird flu scare.

Ada Hadlee, Cambridge

TALKING of bird flu, I recently found a dead swan. I remembered the warnings that accompanied the previous H5N1 scare, so I called the authorities. How foolish I felt when I remembered I was the Queen and the dead swan was my tea.

HM The Queen, e-mail

I RECENTLY saw an article in a woman's magazine entitled 'All Men Are Liars', which was strange because it was opposite an advert for Wonderbra.

Richard Clothier, e-mail

WHY IS IT that cows have got four tits, yet my wife has only got two? It hardly seems fair.

Harold Papercut, Tonbridge

ACCORDING to today's paper, Amy Winehouse's drugs habit has left her battling a life-threatening illness at the tender age of 25. How refreshing to see a pop star getting on with their career in this way. Elvis took three decades to finally wreck his health through high living and Keith Richards is still dragging his decline out after nearly forty years. It just gets boring after a while. I say hats off to Amy Winehouse for pulling her finger out and getting the job done early doors!

Horace Bojangles, Rhyll

Modern Pond Pumps 'No Good on the Moon'

BRITISH WATER PUMP manufacturers were yesterday warned that their products would not function properly if used in the low gravity atmosphere on the moon.

An investigation by scientists at NASA concluded that a traditional pump used in a pond on the moon would squirt the water too high.

"The gravitational pull of the moon is only a quarter that of

MOONSCLUSIVE!

the earth," said Professor Jackson Pallo, head of Lunar Colonisation research at NASA's Kennedy Space Centre. "A pump used in a pond on the moon would send the water four times higher that it would on earth.

And of course, the water would fall back into the pond four times slower. There is a very real danger that the pump would drain the pond before the water fell back in, leaving any goldfish gasping for breath."

TWAT

When we called pop star Sting, who had a hit with *Walking on the Moon*, he said: "I'm in the vinegar strokes. I reckon another hour and a half should do it."

I STARTED knitting my husband a lovely jumper for his birthday, but I ran out of wool after completing just one sleeve. However, later that day my husband's boss phoned me from the zoo where he works and told me that my husband's arm had been ripped off by a polar bear. However, my joy turned to despair when I visited him in hospital, because he'd had the wrong arm pulled off. Well I'm not unpicking it, so he'll just have to wear it inside out or back to front.

Mildred Feathers, Newton

MY WIFE died ten years ago, and try as I might, I still can't help blaming myself for her death. That's because I shot her in the head.

Hector Rampton, Croydon

HAVING seen old footage of screaming girls at concerts given by the Beatles, I can't help wondering if teenage girls were actually terrified of the Fab Four.

Tom Mossop, e-mail

LIKE many others, I enjoyed this latest series of *The Apprentice* with Sir Alan Sugar, but I was disappointed with his catchphrase "You're fired." As a successful businessman, he should know that the contestants are only candidates for the job, and as such, cannot technically be fired. Could I suggest that in the next series, Sir Alan points to the unlucky person and says "We're sorry, but your application has been unsuccessful on this occasion"? It may seem a small point, but it has spoilt my enjoyment of the show.

Chris Knights, e-mail

HOW can we be sure that Don Estelle is really dead, and he's not going to reappear all tearful behind the Sergeant Major, like he did in that episode of *It Ain't Half Hot Mum* when they thought he drowned, but he reappeared reappear all tearful behind the Sergeant Major?

Rodney Bewes, Dundee

HOW come the government wants ordinary people to reduce their carbon footprint, but gives pensioners a winter fuel allowance so as they can heat their bungalows like the reptile house at London Zoo?

CD Stomper, e-mail

THERE'S an actress in *Sea Patrol* on the Hallmark Channel who is the double of Heather Mills. Paul McCartney should have married her instead. Chances are she's not half the harridan that Mills is, and she's got two legs as well.

Seb Rice, Torquay

I'D JUST like to reply to that cheeky arsewipe T. Thorn of Hexham (*Letterbocks* page 51) who was glaring at my son, Anthony Hutton, as he ate his meal on the return flight from New York. What a nosey, impolite, rude and ignorant sod. Don't you realise that's the worst type of manners, staring at someone whilst they eat? Get a life, T. Thorn.

Annette Hutton, address witheld

WITH reference to Annette Hutton's letter (*above*). I wouldn't get too upset on your son's behalf. 5 million people stared at him all day when he was on *Big Brother*. In fact they watched while he slept, had a shit and tried to bang Makosi in the bath. So I don't think one bloke looking at him eat his salad on a plane is going to bother him too much.

T Thorn, Hexham

I WAS IN a cafe the other day and a woman told me that her son had taken up fox hunting as the ban came into force because, he said, "Nobody is going to tell me what I can and can't do." What an arsehole. I hope nobody tells him that he can't put a brick through my car window, or he'll be straight round to do it.

P Osgood, Luton

MORE SECRET PAPERS LOST!

AN ENQUIRY has been launched at the BBC after a file containing sensitive information was left in the back of a taxi. The document, an internal memo between two BBC departments, revealed the name of the football team that 5Live match commentator Alan Green supports.

Green, well known for his catchphrase *"This is woeful, absolutely woeful,"* has never publicly revealed the name of his favourite club. And BBC bosses have vowed to keep the 56-year-old comentator's club a closely guarded secret, insisting it is a 'personal matter.'

"If it were known which club Alan followed, it could compromise his position as a match commentator," said BBC sports editor Mihir Bose. "That this information has been left somewhere public is very embarrassing."

cab

The file was handed to reporters by taxi driver Frank Arsehole, who found it in the back of his cab after picking up a junior rescarcher from Broadcasting House. He said: "I had a quick flick through to see what it was. It was all fairly dull stuff about Jeremy Clarkson's wages and Evan Davis's piercings, but when I saw that it named Green's team, I realised its significance."

slim

BBC bosses were last night reviewing their procedures in a bid

Green (above) ~ yesterday and the secret BBC document at the centre of the row.

'Woeful' lapse of security at the Beeb

to prevent such a security breach happening in future. "The document is back in our possession, and Mr Arsehole has been killed, so no harm has been done on this occasion," a spokesman said last night. "But if this classified information had fallen into the wrong hands and it had come to light that Alan Green is a supporter of that particular club, it could have done untold damage," he added.

FOOL your boss into thinking that your alarm clock is broken by continually turning up late for work in the morning.

Kris Mortimer, e-mail

DON'T throw away old underpants. With the leg holes sewn up and filled with earth, they make smashing hanging baskets for trailing plants.

A Titmarsh, Harrogate

AVOID the constant price increases in milk by buying all you will need for the rest of the year in January.

Iain Finlayson, e-mail

DON'T throw away old string vests. Nailed to the walls outside they make an excellent trellis for climbing plants.

A Titmarsh, Harrogate

EMO kids. Get revenge on everyone that 'doesn't care' by cutting yourself in unseen places. That'll show 'em.

DJ Ants, e-mail

TRANSEXUALS. Make yourself feel more like a woman by driving a car badly whilst talking bollocks.

Grant B Warner, New Malden

DON'T throw away old socks. They can be used to protect cucumbers, marrows and aubergines from early frosts.

A Titmarsh, Harrogate

MORRISSONS supermarket in Whitley Bay. Put a nice 10-foot long canopy in the designated smoking area to keep your employees nice and dry whilst they have their fags. Meanwhile, leave the three spaces for cycles open to the elements.

Troy Hurtubise, Whitley Bay

TRAINSPOTTERS. Type the name of the train you wish to spot into an internet search engine to bring up a picture of it. You can use the time you save to get on with your life.

Senor Beeftrotter, e-mail

toptips@viz.co.uk

BIG VERN

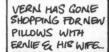

VERN HAS GONE SHOPPING FOR NEW PILLOWS WITH ERNIE & HIS WIFE...

OH... I JUST CAN'T DECIDE WHETHER TO GET THESE GOOSE FEATHER PILLOWS OR THE SLIGHTLY CHEAPER HOLLOW FIBRE ONES, ERNIE. HMM...

I DON'T KNOW EITHER, DEAR. VERN - WHAT DO **YOU** RECKON WE SHOULD DO..?

DO FACKIN' **WOT**, ERNIE!? ER... I WAS JUST WONDERING...

...DO YOU THINK WE SHOULD PLUMP FOR THESE **MAN-MADE** PILLOWS... OR SHOULD WE GET **DOWN**?

GET DAHN, ERNIE...?! YES.

GET DAHN ERNIE!! IT'S THE FACKIN' **FILF**! BUT DON'T WORRY... I'LL NOT LET THE BASTARDS TAKE YOU ALIVE! NO! VERN!

PLUMF!

...AN' I AIN'T DOIN' TIME FER THIS ONE..! **BLAM!**

SCREAM! SCREAM! SCREAM! SCREAM!

BLAM!

LOTTIE LEARNS HOW...

to be in The Fall

WHO IS THAT POP GROUP ON THE TELEVISION, MOTHER? THAT'S THE FALL, LOTTIE. THEY'RE PERFORMING THE 'SONG 'MR PHARMACIST' FROM THEIR 1986 ALBUM, 'BEND SINISTER'.

BEING IN THE FALL KIND OF LOOKS LIKE FUN! I WISH **I** WERE A MEMBER OF THE BAND.

WELL YOU CAN BE LOTTIE - IF YOU'LL FOLLOW A FEW SIMPLE TIPS. **WOW!** IT'S THE FALL'S FRONTMAN, MARK E. SMITH!

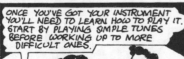

FIRST, YOU'LL NEED A MUSICAL INSTRUMENT. YOU CAN BUY THESE IN YOUR LOCAL MUSIC SHOP. THEY TEND TO BE RATHER EXPENSIVE, SO SHOP AROUND AND COMPARE PRICES TO FIND AN INSTRUMENT WHICH BEST SUITS YOUR BUDGET.

ONCE YOU'VE GOT YOUR INSTRUMENT YOU'LL NEED TO LEARN HOW TO PLAY IT. START BY PLAYING SIMPLE TUNES BEFORE WORKING UP TO MORE DIFFICULT ONES. ASK A GROWN-UP TO HELP YOU PLAY THE TRICKIER SONGS.

TOURING IS A BIG PART OF BEING IN THE FALL, AND SOMETIMES WE PLAY IN COUNTRIES WITH COLD CLIMATES LIKE NORWAY OR GREENLAND. YOU'LL NEED PLENTY OF WARM CLOTHING, SUCH AS SCARVES, WOOLY JUMPERS, MITTENS AND EAR-MUFFS.

NOW YOU'RE ALL SET TO BE IN THE FALL. WELCOME TO THE BAND, LOTTIE! THANKS, MARK E. SMITH! the Fall I'M SICK OF YOU NOW. YOU'RE FIRED.

NEXT WEEK: LOTTIE LEARNS HOW TO BAKE A SPONGE CAKE.

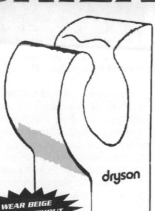

HEAVY METAL rockers AC/DC are once again riding high in the pop charts. Their brand new album *Black Ice*, with its trademark mix of distorted guitars, thumping drums and screaming vocals, has earned rave reviews on both sides of the Atlantic. The band are well known for partying as hard as they play, and tales of their wild excesses on the road are legion.

But one band member's antics leave the others in the shade. For, according to a former roadie, schoolboy guitarist **ANGUS YOUNG** has such an appetite for excess that he is in danger of self-destructing.

GLOBE

After travelling all over the world with the group, Eddie Smalls has seen the havoc that Young has left in his wake in hotels, airports and dressing rooms around the globe. And, he says, it's not a pretty sight.

"I spent 8 years on the road with AC/DC until I got fired for syphoning diesel out of the tour bus, but it wasn't me, it was just someone who looked a bit like me. Actually he looked a lot like me, but it wasn't me," Smalls reveals in his new book.

Young at Heart is a no holds barred account of schoolboy axeman Angus's wild lifestyle as seen at first hand by his closest confidant. And, in this first in a series of exclusive extracts, Eddie finally blows the lid off Young's partying excesses.

JERUSALEM

❝Angus Young certainly earned his reputation as the wild schoolboy of rock. From the early days of AC/DC, he was always the disruptive element in the band. I remember once, during the recording of the album *Dirty Deeds Done Cheap*, he came into the studio looking extremely furtive.

"The sessions got underway, and eventually it was time to record the track *Jailbreak*. The producer rolled the tape and the band started to play. The song was going fine, but when it came time for Young to kick in with his trademark riffing solo, there was silence. Everyone looked round to see what was going on, but Angus was nowhere to be seen!

"We searched the studio from top to bottom but couldn't find him anywhere. We started to get worried. Lead singer Bon Scott was about to call Angus's mum to tell her that he'd gone missing, when the drummer shouted out that he'd found him crouching down behind a speaker stack, looking at a mucky magazine. He'd apparently found it on top of his dad's wardrobe, and decided to smuggle it into the studio up his jumper.

"The producer confiscated the mag and told him he could have it back at the end of the sessions. A red-faced Angus just looked at his shoes and mumbled an apology, before picking up his guitar and carrying on with the recording. But just going back to the stolen diesel, the bloke who took it had exactly the same hair as me, and glasses like mine, and clothes. But it wasn't me. But I can see how the band would of thought that it was me and sacked me, so I don't bear them any grudge or anything."

JAM

The girly magazine episode was soon forgotten, but sadly it was not to be the only time that Young's out-of-control behaviour was to threaten AC/DC's career. Eddie remembers an incident that happened during a UK tour to promote the album *Highway to Hell*.

❝We were on the Scottish leg of the tour. There was always a lot of free time to kill between gigs, and the potential for Angus to get himself into scrapes while he was at a loose end was ever present. The band was staying in Paisley, and there was a lot of worry because Angus had started hanging around with a local tearaway - Wee Jimmy Krankie out of the Krankies. Young seemed to quickly fall under the influence of his new Scottish pal. He was very impressed at the way Jimmy cheeked his elder brother/husband Ian, and he soon started using the word 'Fandabidozy' all the time.

"One night we were performing a big stadium gig. There were thousands of people in the audience and AC/DC were due on stage at eight, but at ten past eight Angus still hadn't turned up. The crowd was getting restless when he finally showed at half past eight ... accompanied by a police officer.

"Apparently, Angus had been caught with Jimmy Krankie on some nearby allotments, where the pair had been running amock, throwing stones at a greenhouse and trampling on some cabbage seedlings. Angus got off lightly, because it was clear that Krankie had been the ringleader in the high-jinks. It was a sheepish Angus Young that took to the stage in Paisley that night, nearly three quarters of an hour late.

SCOTT JOPLIN

"On that occasion, Angus got off with a stern ticking off for his part in the vandalism. But that's more than can be said for me, when that diesel went missing. It wasn't even like it was a lot of diesel, it was only about a couple of gallons. You'd think they could afford to turn a blind eye to a couple of gallons, what with all their millions of record sales. And it wasn't even me that stole it, anyway, as I have already said."

For a while, it seemed that Angus's brush with the law had done the trick, as the wild guitarist seemed to calm down. But he was only biding his time, and it wasn't long before he was getting up to his old tricks again. Eddie remembers one particular time when the guitarist's wild ways nearly ended up with the whole band getting thrown out of a hotel.

UNIVERSITY

❝We were on the California leg of our US tour, staying at the plush Beverly Hills Hilton hotel. One day, the members of the band and road crew decided to go out sightseeing around Hollywood, but Angus told us he wasn't interested. He said our day trip sounded boring, so he was going to stay in his room watching telly and drinking pop out of the mini-bar.

Young a
Hellraising

BREAKING THE RULES:
The schoolboy guitarist's antics threatened to destroy AC/DC, says former roadie Eddie *(right)*.

> "Angus rode his cart down the main staircase into the foyer, through a plate glass window and into the swimming pool"

t Heart
ecrets of AC/DC Angus

"We should of known better than to leave him on his own. When we got back to the Hilton at tea-time, the receptionist had a face like thunder. She called the manager, who told us that because of Angus's behaviour, we were going to have to pack our bags and leave the hotel. We couldn't believe what we were hearing. What had Angus been doing while we were out?

"Apparently, he'd spent the morning mooching about at the Los Angeles municipal dump, where he'd found an old pram, a length of orange twine and some pallets that he'd dragged back to the hotel. Up in his room, he'd made them into a cart which he'd then raced around the hotel corridors, narrowly missing other guests and causing havoc.

"The pandemonium only came to an end after Angus rode his cart down the main staircase into the foy-

er, through a plate glass window and into the swimming pool. It was a stupid thing to do. The furious manager said it was a miracle that nobody had been seriously hurt. Drummer Phil Rudd eventually managed to calm him down with some smooth talking, and we avoided being evicted by the skin of our teeth.

"After that escapade, Young was grounded and had his royalty money stopped for two weeks. Frankly, he got off lightly. If only the band had been as reasonable with me when they caught me syphoning off that diesel. I wouldn't mind, but how much does a couple of gallons of DERV cost, what, about nine quid, something like that? And they've sold 200 million albums at a tenner a pop. That's 2 billion quid and I get fired for nicking nine quids' worth of diesel, and it wasn't even me, anyway."

BOAT RACE

The Donnington Monsters of Rock Festival is the date on the heavy metal calendar when every band wants to give its best performance. But one year, remembers Eddie, Young's insatiable appetite for partying almost led to AC/DC having to pull out of their headline gig at the last minute.

❝It had been Angus's fiftieth birthday, and his mum and dad had allowed him to have a party and a couple of friends stay for a sleepover. Vocalist Brian Johnson wasn't keen on the idea, because he knew that Angus had to be up early the next day to get ready for the big concert. But Young kept pestering him, promising him that he wouldn't overdo it at the party or stay up too late.

"As it happened, Angus's promises were hollow. He didn't show for the soundcheck next morning, and only turned up backstage half an hour before the band were due to go on. He looked like a zombie - he had huge bags under his eyes and he kept complaining that he felt sick. It was clear that the party and sleepover had taken their toll on him.

"One of his pals later confided in me that Angus had been showing off at the party. He'd put away at least thirty fairy cakes and drunk dozens of glasses of blue pop. Afterwards, they'd stayed up until the early hours in his bedroom, playing video games and eating sweets out of their party bags.

I'd never seen him look so wrecked.

"He played the gig, but he stumbled his way through all his solos like he was half asleep, which he was. It was a woeful performance, and the crowd showed their disappointment with a chorus of catcalls and boos. I wasn't surprised. It's not possible to keep up that pace without something giving, and in this case it was his playing that paid the price for his hard-partying lifestyle.

PLATES OF MEAT

"As soon as he got off stage and back on the tour bus, Angus fell fast asleep across the back seat. He must of been absolutely exhausted, because we couldn't wake him up when we got back to his house. His dad, Mr Young, had to carry him off the bus and straight up to bed. He never even got to brush his teeth that night.

"Back on the subject of diesel for a moment, I wouldn't mind, but I was going to pay for it, only I never got the chance because they caught me with the hose in my mouth, put two and two together to make five and sacked me there and then. I only wanted it for my mate who had to take his mam to hospital for an urgent operation, and his van had ran out. And anyway, it wasn't even me."

MINCE PIES

Luckily, AC/DC fans are quite forgiving and the Donnington debacle was soon forgotten. But, says Eddie, Young's behaviour was getting worse, with the guitarist regularly playing truant from rehearsals. On several occasions, vocalist Johnson was forced to go looking for him, more often than not locating the errant guitarist sitting smoking on some swings in the local park or hanging round outside a nearby amusement arcade. And when he did turn up, he was often a disruptive influence. He would fire bits of chewed up blotting paper through a pea-shooter at other bad members and deliberately wee on their shoes whilst standing next to them at the studio urinals. On one occasion he was forced to apologise to AC/DC manager Denis Laughlin after writing 'HOMO' on the back of his coat with a piece of chalk .

But Young's wild excesses reached a crescendo in 1996, when they cost the group their multi-million pound recording contract with EMI.

SATSUMAS

❝The band had been invited to EMI headquarters to sign a lucrative new contract for six albums. There was a massive advance on the table, and all the company big-wigs were going to be there, so Angus was under strict instructions to remain on his best behaviour throughout the meeting. For once, it looked like he'd taken the warnings on board; when he strolled into the reception area he looked positively angelic. He'd got his shirt tucked in, his socks pulled up, his face washed and his hair combed. He'd even polished his shoes!

"But it was all an act. Angus was

just lulling his fellow band members into a false sense of security, as they were to find out when they got into the plush, oak-panelled boardroom on the top floor of the EMI building. While the lawyers, managers and secretaries made their last-minute alterations to the terms and conditions of the deal, Young sat at the end of the table looking as good as gold. Then suddenly, without warning, he reached his hand into his blazer pocket and took out a couple of white mice, a frog and a matchbox containing his pet spider.

"With an impish grin, he released them onto the highly polished boardroom table where they started scurrying and hopping about. It was absolute chaos! Women and lawyers were screaming and desperately trying to clamber up on the chairs to get away from the creepy-crawlies, and the important papers went flying everywhere. It was absolute pandemonium, and Angus was sat there in the middle of it all, laughing his head off.

NUTS

"EMI chairman Sir Anthony Wadsworth was purple-faced with rage. He leapt up from his seat to grab Angus by the scruff of the neck and give him a good old-fashioned clip round the ear, only to fall flat on his face. His shoelaces had "mysteriously" got tied together under the table. By now, the rumpus had attracted the attention of a burly security guard, who burst into the room to see what was going on. Somehow, he managed to trap Angus in the corner of the room, and it looked like it was finally curtains for the mischievous schoolboy rocker.

BOLLOCKS

"But Young suddenly picked up a nearby wastepaper basket and pulled it over the guard's head, before dropping down onto his knees and scampering out through his widely-spaced legs. Pausing only to catapult a couple of eggs at Wadsworth, breaking his glasses and dislodging his toupee, he then took the opportunity to fill the pockets of his shorts with biscuits from the table, before climbing out of the window and making his escape by clambering down a nearby tree. Needless to say, the furious chairman himself tore up the contract, and forbade AC/DC from ever recording on EMI again."

Eddie Small's book, Young at Heart - On the Road with Heavy Metal Monsters of Rock (Muesli Books, £18.99) is available from all good bookshops.

NEXT WEEK: "Anyway, I'd actually put some diesel in the bus with my own money, so how could they sack me for stealing something that was already mine? And anyway, it wasn't even me, it was that other bloke."

GILBERT RATCHET

WOW! LOOK WHO THEY'VE GOT AS CELEBRITY GUEST AT THE VICARAGE FETE!

I'M GOING TO ASK GOD TO AUTOGRAPH THIS CHICKEN, WHICH HE CREATED-ETH ON THE FIFTH DAY

THERE'S GOD WITH THE VICAR AT THE 'SPLAT THE RAT' STALL

DRAT! I'M TRYING TO CATCH GOD'S EYE SO I CAN ASK HIM TO SIGN MY CHICKEN

I'LL CONSTRUCT AN EYE-CONTACT-ESTABLISHER-O-MATIC TO GET GOD'S ATTENTION

GOD IS MY ABSOLUTE HERO. I REALLY ADMIRE THE WAY HE INVENTED THE HEAVEN AND EARTH IN SIX DAYS.

IT'LL BE SO EXCITING TO MEET HIM.

GOSH! HE LOOKS MORE OMNIPRESENT IN REAL LIFE.

BUT BEING THE ULTIMATE CELEBRITY HE IS SKILLED AT AVOIDING THE GAZE OF AUTOGRAPH HUNTERS.

HE'LL BE UNABLE TO IGNORE THE POWERFUL STARE EMANATING FROM THIS GIANT EYEBALL.

OOPS! THE GIANT EYE IS A BIT TRICKY TO CONTROL ~ IT'S DIRECTING ITS GAZE AT THE VICAR INSTEAD

IT'S GAZING RIGHT INTO MY SOUL! STOP IT! GO AWAY!

GO AWAY I TELL YOU!

OH DEAR - GOD APPEARS TO BE DEAD - I'VE BEEN AND GONE AND KILLED HIM WITH ME SPLAT THE RAT BAT.

GASP! WHY IS THAT BIG BEADY EYEBALL STARING AT ME?

STOP PEERING AT MY DARKEST AND MOST SECRET MASTURBATORY FANTASIES!

(WHOOPSY DAISY! I'VE ACCIDENTALLY BASHED THE LORD'S SKULL IN!

REALLY, REVEREND NIETZSCHE! I AM MOST DISPLEASED THAT YOU SNUFFED OUT OUR DIVINE CREATOR.

B-BUT LADY MONEYBAGGS, IT WAS AN ACCIDENT...

THAT'S TORN IT! LADY MONEYBAGGS IS OUR RICHEST PATRON! YOU'VE GOT TO INVENT A REPLACEMENT GOD FOR HER LADYSHIP.

GREAT! I LOVE THE HOOK-A-DUCK STALL! NOW, LET ME SEE...

SILENCE! I AM A DEEPLY RELIGIOUS PERSON, REVEREND.

UNLESS YOU FIND A WAY OF REPLACING GOD, I SHALL MAKE NO MORE DONATIONS TO YOUR CHURCH STEEPLE FUND.

IF YOU DO, I'LL LET YOU HAVE A FREE GO ON THE HOOK-A-DUCK STALL.

WHAT WE NEED IS A KIND OF BEARDED FATHER FIGURE UP IN THE SKY WHICH WILL MAKE LADY MONEYBAGGS FEEL THAT SHE IS SOMEHOW 'SPECIAL'.

I'VE RIGGED UP THIS SELECTIVELY BENEVOLENT DEITY WITH PING-PONG BALL EYES, A FATHERLY PIPE AND A CANDY-FLOSS HAIR AND BEARD COMBINATION.

THERE!

SPLENDID. PRAISE THE LORD!

UH-OH! THE SUGARY CANDY-FLOSS BEARD IS ATTRACTING WASPS!

TSK! I DON'T WANT AN OLD TESTAMENT TYPE OF GOD, WHO WILL TORMENT ME WITH PLAGUES OF WASPS AND STINGS ON THE BOTTOM!

WHAT I REALLY WANT IS THE REASSURANCE OF AN ALL-KNOWING SUPREME BEING. I WANT TO KNOW THAT THERE IS A MYSTICAL FORCE UP THERE WHICH HAS ALL THE ANSWERS.

THAT SHOULD SATISFY YOUR RELIGIOUS YEARNINGS.

AND ONE OF THEM'S STUNG HER LADYSHIP ON THE ARSE!

YOU'LL HAVE TO DO BETTER THAN THAT IF YOU WANT A FREE GO ON THE HOOK-A-DUCK STALL, GILBERT!

COMING RIGHT UP, YOUR LADYSHIP!

IT'S A SET OF ENCYCLOPEDIAS ON STILTS, ENVELOPED IN A SPOOKY DRY-ICE MIST.

OOH, I SAY! HOW INEFFABLE!

OH DEAR ~ I MUST'VE WIRED UP THE DRY-ICE MACHINE WRONGLY

WOW! NOW THE WHOLE THING'S ABLAZE!

QUICKLY REVEREND NIETZSCHE TAKE £100 FOR THE STEEPLE FUND ~ IN FACT, TAKE £200!

NICE WORK, GILBERT. COME ON, THE HOOK-A-DUCK STALL IS OVER HERE.

THERE YOU GO, SON. ONE WEB-FOOTED AQUATIC BIRD PROSTITUTE WHOSE CAR ENGINE HAS SUDDENLY FAILED DUE EITHER TO INCORRECT USE OF THE CLUTCH, OR POSSIBLY INCORRECT ADJUSTMENT OF THE FUEL MIXTURE.

THERE'S ALL SPARKS COMING OUT OF IT.

SCREAM! MY NEW GOD APPEARS TO BE ANGRY WITH ME!

ANYTHING TO SAVE ME FROM THE ETERNAL FIRES OF DAMNATION

HOORAY!

AW, FLIP! IT'S THAT SORT OF "HOOKER DUCK STALL".

NOBBY'S PILES

NOW THEN, MR GILES, THIS MAY SMART A LITTLE...

THE CHUFFIELD PRIVATE CLINIC HAEMORRHOID CURES NOW AVAILABLE ENQUIRE WITHIN

GAAAAAA! FUCKING JESUS!!

WAITING ROOM

SURGERY 1

WEEK PUNCH

THERE YOU GO. YOUR COURSE OF TREATMENT IS COMPLETE... I'VE PUSHED YOUR ADRIANS RIGHT BACK UP.

≥PHEW!≤

NOW THE SPECIAL GLUE TAKES A SHORT WHILE TO FULLY SET, SO IT'S BEST IF YOU AVOID SNEEZING FOR THE NEXT FEW MINUTES.

THANKS DOC.

...YOU KNOW WHAT, DEAR? MY NIPSY HASN'T FELT THIS GOOD FOR YEARS! THAT'S THE BEST £20,000 I EVER SPENT!

ye olde SNUFF SHOP

CAT BARBERS

WORLD PEPPER GRINDING RECORD ATTEMPT

ALL-IN WRESTLERS KING-SIZE MATTRESS BEATING SERVICE

103

LETTERBOCKS

Viz Comic
PO Box 656
North Shields
NE30 4XX

letters@viz.co.uk

This page guest edited by House of Horrors nut job Rose West

"Hi! Rose West out of The House of Horrors here. You know, I was thrilled to be asked to guest edit this Viz Letterbocks page, but I didn't realise what hard work it would be. It's been murder trying to whittle down the thousands of letters I've received. In fact, I think **sewing** mailbags is easier than **editing** them! Anyway, here are the letters I've selected. And the sender of Rose's Star Letter wins a copy of my autobiography, 'A Rose by Any Other West.' I haven't quite finished it yet, and when I do, I've got to find a publisher. But as soon as I've done that, a copy will be on its way." — Rose x

ROSE'S STAR LETTER

MY HUSBAND is a keen nudist, and he's forever accidentally stabbing his penis with his fork whilst cooking sausages on the barbecue. To get over this problem, I now write the words 'Your Cock' on his penis and 'Not Your Cock' on his sausages with a marker pen every time he lights the barbecue.

Mrs A Read, Halifax

A MATE of mine was going out with this German girl who, during a particularly frenzied sex session, shouted out "Fuck me hardly!" This made my friend laugh so much it put him off his stroke. Have any of your other readers ever been at it with a continental girl and encountered amusingly bad English during the coital act?

Puffy McDuffy, e-mail

COULD I take this opportunity to remind the UKTV History channel that a lot of history happened before 1939, and a substantial amount of it has also happened since 1945. Not only that, some of it didn't happen in Germany.

A Thackray, e-mail

ON A previous Letterbocks page I read with glee a letter from one of my many fans. I am of course cheeky geordie Big Brother legend Anthony. It was a chap who said he spotted me eating and he watched me eat my meal. My mum wrote in to complain but now I want to thank the fan and say I actually enjoyed him watching me eat. If he wants to get in contact with me then I would love to go for a meal and watch him watching me eat.

Anthony Hutton, Newcastle

IN ALL this debate about the future of the Church of England, I find myself siding firmly with the traditionalists. It seems obvious to me that women can't be bishops as they would be moody from their periods all the time. And gay men should never be allowed to be priests as they'd spend all day thinking about men's bottoms and never get any work done.

Chris T Martini, e-mail

AM I the first reader to spot Jimmy Hill at the counter in the police station, in frame 12 of the Fat Slags cartoon in Viz 177? If I am, then it must be a miracle as I never win fuck all, me.

Mark Hopkinson, e-mail

Congratulations, Mark. You win fuck all.

I WONDER if someone could put my mind at ease. I visited the Jorvik Viking Centre in York at the weekend and went on their Time Machine, back to Viking days. As we returned to the present, the voicover announced "... and here we are, back in the 1980s". I am now extremely worried that I have become stranded in the recent-ish past. What year is this? How will I ever get back home?

R Crompton, Halifax

HOW about a picture of a squirrel driving a go-kart?

Craig Wardle, Newcastle

Here you go, Craig.

WHEN I was a little girl, I would ask my mother what was for tea and each day she would say "Why don't you fuck off and mind your own fucking business." It was always rhubarb crumble! I'm now over a hundred years old and to this day, rhubarb crumble is known as "Why don't you fuck off and mind your own fucking business" in our family!

Edna Tortoise, Frome

ISN'T IT about time that nature programmes stopped banging on about all these species endangered by man? Ask that bloke who got stang off a shark or my mate James Morley who got bitten on the tit off a horse. If you want my opinion, extinction's too good for them.

George Lennan, e-mail

ANY chance of you bringing back the Lames to Fame? It's just that on a recent trip to see the parents, I found out that my brother's ex-fiancee's new boyfriend had once held the world record for putting pegs on his face.

Andy Fairhurst, e-mail

WALKING through the cheese section of Morrisons in Reddish yesterday, I overheard a girl pointing at a packet of Leerdammer and saying "Look, it sounds exactly the same as Lee Adama, you know, out of Battlestar Galactica." Her friend rolled her eyes and walked off. I wonder if any of your readers can think of another fictional character

SCAB!!

UNISON EQUAL RIGHTS!

UNISON FAIR PAY!

THAT'S AN IMPRESSIVE STRIKE FROM THE CENTRE FORWARD

Top Tips

WINDOW CLEANERS. When agreeing a price with Dr Who to clean the windows of the Tardis, don't be conned into agreeing to do the insides for the same price.

Grant B Warner, New Malden

DRIVERS. Drop gravel into your fuel tank so you can fill your car up for less at the petrol station.

Frank Randle, Clitheroe

NUDISTS. Keep your testicles cosy and warm during cold snaps by popping your scrotum into a "string vest" made from one of those net bags you get with washing tablets.

Al Read, Halifax

HOUSEWIVES. Here's a splendid way of making your cooking oil go further. Simply leave it on the No.87 bus on the way home from the shops.

Geraint Crindle, Liverpool

PARTY HOSTESSES. Cactus plants make excellent buffet sausage dispensers if you've run out of grapefruits and cocktail sticks.

Mrs Wilton, Rochdale

NUDISTS. In cold weather, when you are forced to wear clothes, simply pin a photograph of your cock and balls onto the front of your trousers.

Al Read, Halifax

BBC1's former *One Show* presenter Adrian Chiles would just need a curly wig and red lipstick, Portsmouth FC manager Harry Redknapp would simply require a feather boa, but I'm struggling to think of a third celebrity who could be transformed into a pantomime dame within 30 seconds. Can any of your readers help?

S Maguire, e-mail

IN RESPONSE to R Crompton letter (*opposite page*) about her visit to the Jorvik Centre, do not worry. The so-called Time Machine is merely a poor-quality ride which nobody has bothered to update since the 1980s. This explains the slow journey it takes you on, through a tacky looking scene occupied by badly-rendered wax figures who all have one mechanical arm hovering up and down, either near a plank of wood to indicate a craftsman, or near some food to indicate a cook.

C Martin, London

SOME BLOKE came up to me in the street yesterday and asked me if I had heard the good news. I couldn't wait to hear what exciting and wonderful thing had happened, so imagine my disappointment when it turned out to be that if I do exactly what God tells me, I won't burn in hell forever.

Martin Pickwick, Tuinbridge

ON THE subject of religion, is there any chance of seeing that picture of the Pope kissing that bird's tit again please?

Lee Irving, e-mail

whose first and second names together sound just like a well known type of cheese. I've spent 34 hours on it so far, and I haven't got a fucking clue.

OCD, Stockport

Can you think of someone in a book, film, TV show or play who sounds like a type of cheese? Perhaps there's a nymphomaniac three-day-eventer in Jilly Cooper's book Riders called Sage Derby. Or maybe you listen to The Archers and there's a new gigolo hanging round the Bull called Monty Veronese. Or is there a minor character in Peter Schaffer's play Equus called Crack O'Barrel? Write in and let us know at the usual address. There's 6 pounds of cheese and a packet of Tesco Value Water Biscuits for every one we print.

L'OREAL adverts claim that their conditioner makes your hair up to 70% softer. Then underneath, in very small writing, they go on to say that this is in comparison to no conditioner. Call me fussy, but shouldn't a product be at least 100% more effective than nothing?

Christina Martin, e-mail

IF I worked for the Samaritans, I'd advise anyone calling in and threatening suicide to go and have a shit. I always feel better after a shit.

David Hammond, e-mail

Sender: Howard Gooding, London

SACHSGATE VOX POP

IT'S THE TOPIC that everyone can't stop talking about six weeks ago. Jonathan Ross and Russell Brand's obscene phone calls to veteran actor Manuel stirred up a storm of outrage. BBC complaint lines went into meltdown as millions of licence payers called in to register their disgust at the foul-mouthed prank. To many, the incident was the worst atrocity ever perpetrated on Radio 2, and it has even led to calls from the Prime Minister for the pair to be sacked. Undoubtedly Brand and Ross are highly talented, quick-witted comedians, except Brand. And Ross. But is it worth ending two glittering careers for what was perhaps at worst a momentary lapse of judgement? In fact, do comedians have a duty to push back the boundaries of comedy and taste? We went on the street to assess the mood of the British public...

...I DON'T know what Andrew Sachs is complaining about. If he doesn't like Brand and Ross's style of humour, he doesn't have to listen to it. After all, there is an off button on his answering machine.

Robert Kilwardby, florist

...GORDON Brown has had his say on this sorry affair and I believe it is now time for Her Majesty the Queen to take action. She should strip Ross of the OBE with which he was recently honoured and replace it with a slightly less prestigious MBE.

Walter Reynolds, gynaeocologist's mate

...I DISAGREE. The Queen should stay out of the argument as it would be too distressing for her. She is a grandmother herself, and I can only imagine how upset she would be if Brand phoned her up and said he'd fucked Princess Eugenie.

Tom Brawardine, hypnotherapist

...I ENJOY a healthy sex life with my wife, but in 15 years of marriage I have never once felt the need to phone her grandfather and leave a filth-filled, four-letter message on his answerphone detailing what we get up to in bed. I tend to use euphemisms, such as 'hiding the sausage', 'kicking her back doors in' and 'sipping from the hairy cup'.

Edmund Grindal, jam taster

...I COULD understand that phoning the Queen to tell her that you had fucked Princess Eugenie would be unacceptable and inappropriate. However, if it was Zara Phillips who'd been on the end of your cock, it would be understandable that you would want to tell as many people as possible.

Thomas Arundel, ice cream man

...ROSS has gone too far this time and overstepped the bounds of decency. And top marks to the BBC for slashing his £18million salary to £17million. They have shown that they mean business by hitting him where it hurts... in the loose change.

Fred Cornwallis, kinesiologist

...ROSS bought flowers for Andrew Sachs by way of an apology. But it was the entire nation that was offended by the broadcast, not just the Manuel actor. To make amends with the public, Ross should buy a bunch of flowers for everyone in Britain and deliver them personally. I'm not in on Wednesdays, but Mrs Depledge next door could take them in for me.

Roger Walden, locksmith

...I AGREE with Mr Walden (above), but I do my bowls league on Tuesdays and Thursdays. Could Ross leave my flowers just behind the wheelie bin, please?

Henry Dean, male model

...ROSS will not be able to buy my forgiveness with a bunch of flowers. When my bouquet arrives, I'm going to put my foot through it and send him the bill.

Thomas Cranmer, nail technician

...Mr Cranmer (above) seems to forget that there were two people involved in this sordid stunt. I will be putting my foot through my bouquet and sending a bill for 50% of the cost each to Jonathan Ross and Russell Brand respectively.

Richard Bancroft, osteopath

...I SUFFER from terrible hay fever. Could I have chocolates instead?

Gilberta Sheldon, potato merchant

...I'M GOING to wait until Brand has a child and that child has a daughter. Then, when she reaches the age of 16, I'm going to fuck her and then phone Brand up and tell him what I've done. See how he likes it.

Matthew Hutton, quantity surveyor

...WHAT people are forgetting is that the real hypocrite in this sorry affair is Sachs himself. He has regularly had sex with his wife and I dare say he has never told her grandfather about it. At least Brand had the common decency to admit what he had done.

Archibald Tait, roustabout

...THE BBC should tear up both their contracts. I work in a British Gas call centre, and if I shouted obscenities down the phone to members of the public I would be sacked on the spot. So I write their names and addresses down and send them a turd in the post.

John Whitgift, stockbroker

...UNLIKE the previous writer, I work manning the phones for sex chat line company, and I would lose my job if I DIDN'T shout obscenities at members of the public.

Enid Depledge, genuine randy granny

...THE PERSON who has shown the biggest lack of judgement in this case is Georgina Baillie in having sex with Russell Brand in the first place. What was she thinking of?

Vagina Fitzjocelin, unicyclist

...I DON'T think that it is enough that Russell Brand has quit, Jonathan Ross has been suspended and the director of Radio 2 has been forced to resign over Manuelgate. Surely Gordon Brown has to go too. After all, he was Prime Minister when this sorry affair happened.

Hubert Walter, violinist

...ROSS and Brand making obscene phone calls to a harmless old man amounts to nothing more than corporate bullying. It was the worst breach of taste, decency and judgement ever perpetrated in the name of entertainment. Only the severest disciplinary sanctions will assuage the public's disgust at this despicable broadcast. The BBC must act now and act decisively, and quickly sack a junior assistant producer.

Stephen Langton, xylophone tuner

...BRAND and Ross are no better than paedophiles and rapists. They should both be chemically castrated and put on the sex offenders register.

Ralph Neville, yogi

...THE PREVIOUS writer suggesting this despicable pair be put on the sex offenders register is nonsense. The sex offenders' register these days is like a holiday camp. Ross and Brand should have their bell ends fed into an office paper shredder. And I'd push the 'ON' button myself.

Boniface of Savoy, zebra trainer

...HAVING their bell ends fed into office paper shredders would be no punishment for the likes of these two, who would revel in the publicity that such an action would bring them. They should be injected with AIDS and put on an island where the RAF could use them for bombing practice.

Sir Peter de la Bilious, Wing Commander

...RIGHTY-HO, FRUBERT LOVE, I'LL BE OFF THEN.

HMMM..?

I'M GOING INTO HOSPITAL FOR MY HIP REPLACEMENTS, REMEMBER? ...AND MY... LADIES' OPERATIONS.

OH YEAH. 'BYE THEN.

=COUGH=

...YOU STILL HERE?

THESE ARE RISKY PROCEDURES, FRUBERT. I'LL BE AWAY FOR A MONTH AND A HALF. I'M A BIT SCARED...

WELL DON'T BE...

HONESTLY— I'LL BE FINE.

SLAM!

HEH-HEH!... I'LL BE FINE, ALRIGHT...! I'VE GOT A SIX WEEK PINK TICKET!

BACK OF THE OVEN!

...TALKING OF WHICH... IT'S ABOUT TIME I GOT BAKING MESELF A BIT OF GINGERBREAD CRUMPET!

FLOUR

SHORTLY...

TING!

GAW! SHE'S READY!

COME IN, MY DEAR... WE'VE GOT THE HOUSE TO OURSELVES...! =SLURP!=

WHAT'S THAT YOU SAY? WHERE'S MY WIFE..? DON'T WORRY YOUR PRETTY LITTLE BISCUIT HEAD... SHE WON'T DISTURB US. SHE'S... SHE'S...ER...

...SHE'S DEAD.

YOU'RE VERY SORRY TO HEAR THAT, YOU SAY..? WELL DON'T BE. YOU SEE, OUR MARRIAGE WAS NOTHING BUT A HOLLOW SHAM!

WE'D GROWN APART, YOU SEE. THERE WAS NO EXCITEMENT LEFT IN OUR RELATIONSHIP.

=HEH-HEH= NICE ONE FRUBERT, PLAYING ON HER HEARTSTRINGS LIKE THAT. SHE'S FALLEN FOR IT HOOK, LINE AND SINKER. SHE'S MARZIPAN IN YOUR HANDS!

=SNIFF=

WHAT'S THAT, MY DEAR..? WHY DON'T YOU TAKE ME UPSTAIRS TO SHOW ME SOME OF THE AFFECTION I'VE BEEN MISSING..?

...AND EMPTY MY POOR, ACHING BAKER'S NUTS FOR ME..?

...UH-UH! UH-UH! UH-UH-UH-UH... UH-UH-UH-UH...

...UH-UH-UH-UH..! UHUHUHUHUHUH..! UHUHUHUHUHUHUHUHUHUHUHUH... EEEEEUUUUUUUUURGH!!

WOW! THAT WAS AMAZING! MY WIFE NEVER LETS ME DO THAT TO HER, THE FRIGID BITCH.

...I MEAN, SHE NEVER USED TO LET ME DO THAT TO HER WHEN SHE WAS ALIVE, GOD REST HER SOUL.

WHAT'S THAT..? NO, I CAN'T IMAGINE THIS RELATIONSHIP EVER GROWING STALE EITHER, MY LOVE...

=SIGH!=

6 WEEKS LATER...

=HRRUMPH=

CONTINUED OVER

111

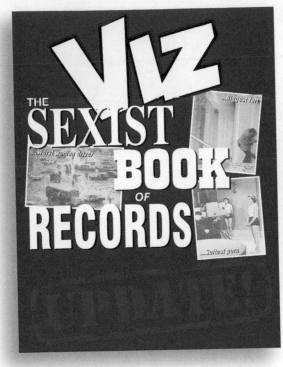

The World of Women

Night-Time Beauty Regime

The longest night-time beauty regime for a woman is one of 14hr 12min, practiced by Kylie Bradwell (GB) of Luton. The marathon exercise begins each night at 6.00pm when Ms Bradwell goes to bed, and the ensuing 7 hours sees her use 148 products to remove the day's make-up. The following 7 hours and 12 minutes is then taken up applying over 193 moisturisers, night creams, ungents and collagen-rich skin enhancers. She finally gets to bed at 8.12 the following morning.

- Cosmetic counter - A selection of some of the hundreds of beauty products that Kylie Bradwell applies to her skin on a nightly basis.

Longest diet

The longest diet ever embarked upon is one of 75yrs 6mths 2days, by Edith Bootree (GB) of Preston. At the age of 18 and weighing 98kg *14st 8lb*, Mrs Bootree bought a size 8 dress in a sale at her local Co-op. She then spent the next 75½ years attempting to slim into it, avoiding all fatty foods, but allowing herself the occasional treat. Over the course of her marathon weight-loss attempt, she tried over 286 faddy diets including the Atkin's, the Hay, the G-plan, the California and the Vanessa Feltz. She briefly lost 250g *8oz* in 1948 but quickly put it back on after celebrating with a chocolate eclair. Her diet eventually came to an end in March 2007 when she died weighing 98kg *14st 8lb*.

Make-up application

The longest make-up application regime for a woman is one of 9hr 30min undertaken by Kylie Bradwell (GB) of Luton. Rising at 8.30 each morning, Ms Bradwell begins to beautify herself with no less that 418 different foundations, blushers, highlighters, lowlighters, contour creams, eye shadows and lip glosses, stopping only to use the toilet.

The World of Men

Least Manly Sandwich

The most effeminate male-purchased sandwich was one ordered on 12th July 2006 by Grant Whistler (GB) in a delicatessen in Chelsea. It comprised of mixed salad leaves including rocket, radicchio and lambs' lettuce, sliced brie and fig relish in a balsamic vinegar dressing. Mr Whistler, a theatre choreographer, made things worse by having it on a wholemeal ciabatta finger roll.

Shiniest suit

A suit belonging to Alf Normans (GB) of Manchester is the recorded as being the shiniest in the world. The arse of the trousers has a reflectance value of 98.32%, which is equivalent to the reflective property of a silver coated mirror being struck by polarized light of a wavelength of 1000nm. Mr Normans bought the suit in 1939 for his wedding and has worn it for his daily visits to the betting shop ever since without once taking it to the dry cleaners.

Lingerie Optimism

The most optimistic male purchase of ladies' underwear was made on the 18th December 2006 by Albert Plywood (GB). Aroused by a window display in the Derby city centre branch of La Senza, Plywood went in to buy something as a Christmas gift for his wife. The outfit, which consisted of a black, sheer-lace basque with balconette bra cups, matching heart-shaped thong and sheer Chantilly lace-topped stockings, cost him a total of £122.99. However, on Christmas day the gift did not go down well with his 58-year-old wife Maureen, who tutted and used them as dusters.

Mental Undressing

The record for the longest time that a man has resisted the temptation to mentally undress a nurse was set by Barry Haddock (GB) of Yorkshire. On 18th March 1993 at Leeds General Infirmary, Mr Haddock watched three nurses wheeling his wife Janice into the operating theatre for a routine operation. It took a full 8.6 seconds before, in his mind's eye, all three nurses were naked except for stockings, suspenders, high-heeled shoes and nurses' hats.

• Ooh, Matron - Barry Haddock of Leeds showed remarkable restraint when his wife was having an op.

Jazz film endurance

The world record for the longest time a man has trod water through a porn film is held by Manuel Espadrille (USA) who, on 16th August 2007, gently strummed through all 85 minutes of *Cock Hungry Nymphos* without fast-forwarding the DVD at any point, finally ejaculating as the credits came up. The British record is held by Lupin Sinstadt (GB) who, on 12th July 1999 on the BBC *Record Breakers* programme successfully watched 48 minutes of *Cum Stained Casting Couch* before going off.

Pornographic magazine

The most expensive pornographic magazine ever purchased was a copy of the December 2002 is-

Schoolboy Sexual Boasting Record Smashed

A NUNEATON schoolboy today smashed the record for the most outlandish sexual boast ever made.

In a playground conversation with several of his Year 10 friends, 14-year-old Ed Tiptree claimed to have bedded over 780 women, including 27 teachers at the school, most of the sixth form, several mothers of friends, the woodwork teacher's daughter and 50 girls he met at Butlins in the summer.

overjoyed

Staff at the Sir Les Patterson High School said they were overjoyed with the school-boy's feat, which broke a national sexual boasting record made 28 years ago.

assembly

Tiptree's achievement was recognised by the headmaster at a special assembly where he received a certificate of commendation. He also received a cup, presented by the former record holder, 42-year-old Terry French who, in 1980, claimed that he "must of knobbed about 500 birds at least. Probably nearer 600."

sue of *Escort*, which cost its buyer a staggering £854.97. On November 14th 2002, Denis Architrave (GB) of Chester went into his local branch of Fourboys Newsagent with the intention of purchasing the Christmas edition of the erotic periodical, which had a cover price of £1.85. However, spotting a friend of his mother's talking to the shop assistant, Mr Architrave bought a packet of chewing gum and a tube of Pringles instead. He returned 10 minutes later but left with a box of Roses chocolates and a packet of pipecleaners after seeing his old primary school headmistress at the counter, paying her paper bill. Over the course of the following three weeks, Mr Architrave continued to visit the shop at approximately 10-minute intervals, but was thwarted at each attempt and forced to make a decoy purchase, eventually running up his record-breaking bill. He finally managed to purchase his copy of *Escort* on December 5th 2002 having amassed, during the preceding 21 days, a haul of unwanted goods including 706 packets of chewing gum, 36 bottles of Dandelion & Burdock, 112 Bic Biros, 355 spiral-bound reporters' notebooks, 45 combs and a pencil sharpener.

Sneaking a Peek

The longest that a man has managed to maintain eye contact with a woman during a conversation without surreptitiously glancing at her breasts is held by Barry Haddock (GB) of Yorkshire. On the 18th March 1993 at Leeds General Infirmary, whilst being informed of his wife Janice's death during a routine operation, Mr Haddock managed to look the nurse in the eye for 14.1 seconds before his eyes briefly checked out her knockers.

Foreign film endurance

The greatest number of unintelligible foreign films a man has sat through in an attempt to get into a woman's knickers is 6. On August 23rd 2008, Michael Bavistock (GB), a plasterer's labourer from Hackney, went on a cinema date with librarian Lucy Watmough. Rather than see *The Art of War 2* starring Wesley Snipes, he agreed to attend a screening of *L'Age d'Or* at the local art house cinema. In the same week, he accompanied her to viewings of *Boudu Sauve des Eaux*, *Doktor Mabuse der Spieler*, *Les Yeux Sans Visage*, *Kumonosu-jo* and *Zero de Conduit*. On the following evening, she asked him if he'd go with her to see *Ai No Corrida*, but seeing as he had not even had a cloth tit, he declined.

The Sexist Book of Records

THE MODERN PARENTS

©John Fardell

Eddie, it's great that Tarquin and Guin are coming round for Amy's birthday, but did we have to invite your sister Cressida and that prat Malcolm?

Don't worry, Julie. Surely not even Cressida and Malcolm would spoil a two-year-old's birthday party...

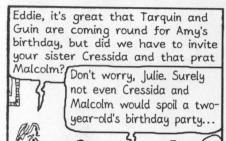

Shortly...

Happy birthday to you, happy birthday to you, happy birthday dear Amy, happy birthday to you.

Oh dear. I'm afraid those candles are making a significant contribution to global warming.

Two tiny birthday cake candles?

Tarquin, that's not the point. Everybody has to do their bit. And we have to set an example.

Yes, now that people in India and China are demanding to have birthday cake candles, the overall effect will be catstrophic. I'm sure Amy doesn't want you to celebrate her birthday by helping to murder the planet.

And I hope that cake's made from organic and vegan ingredients.

And it is wheat-free, isn't it? You know I'm gluten intolerant.

If you don't like the cake, you don't have to have any.

Oh, so now you're discriminating against me because I'm a member of the digestively disabled community. That's illegal!

Malcolm, calm down. How about we watch Amy open some of her presents now?

We've bought Amy a present: It's called an unwrapped present. Instead of wasting money on some piece of consumerist junk, we've gifted the money to a project that's working to make the world a better place. See, here's Amy's certificate.

Look, Amy. Aunty Cressida and Uncle Malcolm have given some money to charity. And for your birthday, they've given you a bit of paper to make sure we all know they've done it.

Julie, we've made the gift in Amy's name. The certificate is a really personal present for her to treasure.

We know, we know. And it's very kind of you. I'm sure these Oxfam Give-a-goat-to-an-African-village projects do loads of good.

Oh, but we wouldn't give money to help Third World villages exploit animals. We made Amy's gift to a much more sound charity — our own Malcolm and Cressida Ethical Living Foundation.

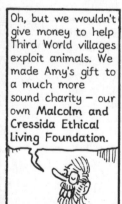

That's not a charity! You mean you've just given the money to yourselves, don't you?

Tarquin, our ethical and environmental lifestyle is a unique grass-roots project: an inspirational example for thousands of others.

Well, Guin and me have bought Amy a proper present.

Here, Amy.

Bear!

Oh, that's really lovely, boys! Thank you very much.

Oh, Tarquin! Teddy bears are an anthropomorphised misrepresentation of wild animals, which brainwash children into thinking that the natural world should be tamed and enslaved by mankind.

Also, teddy bears are deeply offensive to Sudanese people, who are struggling to defend their culture against Western Imperialism. Don't you ever watch the news?

And all soft toys are produced in child labour sweatshops and highly polluting factories. I'm sure Amy wants us to put this hideous teddy in the recyling bin, to at least partly reduce its carbon footprint.

SNATCH!

WAAAH!

CLUNK!

OW! My nose! I think it's bleeding! It's setting off my Sensitive Person's Disorder Syndrome!

Edward, all those awful television programmes you let Amy watch have clearly turned her into violent little monster! We're leaving!

SLAM!

Cheers, Amy. Happy Birthday!

Stars Salute So-Brave Alan

STARS FROM the worlds of stage and screen packed the Cafe Royal last night for the presentation of the 14th annual People of Courage Awards. **PIERS MORGAN, HENRY KISSINGER** and **RIGHT SAID FRED** were amongst the celebrities presenting the honours, given each year to ordinary people who, in the opinion of the judges, have shown outstanding bravery.

And this year the evening's top award was was given to a 38-year old Manchester man. Alan McGarrity received the 'Daily Star Special People's Award for Outstanding Bravery 2008' after what the judges described as "a remarkable year of consistent achievement in the twin fields of courage and fortitude". The honour caps a remarkable 12 months for Mr McGarrity in which he:

• Held up a high street bank **IN BROAD DAYLIGHT** without back up and armed only with a sawn off shotgun.

• Led police on a death-defying high speed car chase the **WRONG WAY** through 15 miles of heavy traffic whilst trying to avoid arrest.

• Had a go at **4 GUARDS** with a pool cue at HM Prison Highdown in Sutton.

McGarrity, currently serving 30 years to life for a series of violent and armed crimes, was unable to at-

■ *By* INGLEDEW BOTTERILL

tend the ceremony after killjoy prison bosses refused to let him out to collect his award in person. Accepting it on Alan's behalf, Ray McGarrity paid tribute to his brother's courage. Fighting back tears, he told the audience:

"If an ordinary person's tyres were burst by a police stinger, they would put their hands in the air and give up. Not Alan. Alan drove twelve more miles on the rims at breakneck speed through crowded streets, often on the pavement. He never gave a thought for his own safety."

He continued: "If you or me were banged up seven years, we'd probably just do our time and keep our noses clean. Not my brother. He had the guts to take a prison psychologist hostage and keep armed guards at bay using just a knife and fork stolen from the kitchen."

"And if our radio privileges were taken from us following a boiling water and sugar attack on another inmate, we'd probably just accept it. Not Alan. He behaved like the true hero, barricading himself and two other prisoners into his cell and setting fire to the mattress," he said.

"It takes a special kind of bravery to do what you think is right when everyone else is telling you it's wrong. And Alan has that kind of bravery," he added.

Other courageous winners on the night included 13-year-old Craig Norvegicus who was caught on CCTV riding the roof of a West Coast mainline train with his hands just inches from the power cables. Jordan Plywood and Kyle Fibreboard from Barnsley were honoured for their heroic 40mph downhill joyride in a shopping trolley which saw them catapulted across a dual carriageway. And a special posthumous award was given to the late Robert Chipboard from Eastbourne, who leapt a remarkable 530 feet to his death from the top of cliffs at Beachy Head after his girlfriend dumped him.

CAUGHT ON CAMERA: McGarrity celebrating his win in prison.

JACK BLACK AND THE SHIT TICKET PUZZLE

THE COUPLE-OF-WEEKS-AFTER EASTER HOLIDAYS WERE HERE ONCE MORE AND JACK BLACK AND SILVER HAD GONE TO STAY WITH AUNT MEG AT HER COTTAGE IN THE SLEEPY YORKSHIRE COTSWOLDS MINING VILLAGE OF CHORLTON-ON-THE-WHEELIE.

DIE ENGLISCHER PIG-DOG! YOUR PUNY SPITFIRE IS NO MATCH FOR THE MIGHT OF THE GLORIOUS NAZI LUFTWAFFE!

DAKKA! DAKKA! DAKKA! AAAAIIEEE!

WOOF!

JACK! JACK! ARE YOU DOWN THERE, LOVE?

AUNT MEG...?

WHAT IS IT, AUNT MEG?

WE'RE OUT OF TOILET PAPER. AGAIN!

IS THERE ANOTHER ROLL DOWN THERE?

NO THERE ISN'T. SORRY.

OH DEAR, DEAR! I'M GOING TO HAVE TO WIPE MY RING WITH THE CARDBOARD TUBE AGAIN. THAT'S THE FOURTH TIME THIS WEEK. I DON'T KNOW WHERE ALL THE PAPER IS GOING.

NEXT MORNING.

GOSH! LOOK AT THIS! IT'S A PROGRAMME ABOUT KEYHOLE SURGERY...

OOOH! GROAN!

...THIS DOCTOR IS USING REMOTE CONTROL SURGICAL INSTRUMENTS TO CARRY OUT OPERATIONS. SIT DOWN AND WATCH IT WITH ME.

I'M AFRAID I CAN'T SIT DOWN ANYWHERE. I'VE GOT THE MOST DREADFUL PILES FROM WIPING MY NIPSY WITH CARDBOARD ALL WEEK. I'M SURPRISED I HAVEN'T HAD A RECTAL PROLAPSE.

OH DEAR!

I'M WALKING ROUND LIKE JOHN RUDDY WAYNE HERE.

BE A LOVE, WOULD YOU, JACK. POP DOWN TO MR MITCHELL'S GARAGE AND GET ME AN INNER TUBE FOR A MORRIS MINOR. I'VE GOT TO HAVE SOMETHING TO SIT ON TO RELIEVE MY JEREMY KYLES. AND FETCH ANOTHER ROLL OF BUMWAD FROM THE VILLAGE SHOP WHILE YOU'RE OUT.

OF COURSE. COME ON, SILVER.

SHORTLY.

HELLO THERE, YOUNG JACK. WHAT CAN I DO FOR YOU?

MITCHELL'S GARAGE

WHEEL BALANCING £5

I'D LIKE TO BUY A MORRIS MINOR INNER TUBE, MR MITCHELL.

ARSE GRAPES, IS IT?

NOT ME. AUNT MEG! BUT HOW DID YOU KNOW.

EVERYONE IN THE VILLAGE HAS GOT THEM. I'VE SOLD MORE OF THESE THINGS THIS WEEK THAN IN THE WHOLE OF THE LAST TEN YEARS.

WOW!

THERE YOU GO. THAT'LL BE BLESSED RELIEF FOR YOUR AUNT MEG.

THANKS, MR MITCHELL. HOW MUCH DO I OWE YOU?

FIFTEEN POUNDS.

FIFTEEN POUNDS! THAT'S ROBBERY!

IT'S SUPPLY AND DEMAND, JACK, SO MANY PEOPLE WANT THESE THAT I'VE BEEN ABLE TO QUADRUPLE THE PRICE.

ANYWAY, YOU'LL HAVE TO EXCUSE ME, I'VE GOT ANOTHER CUSTOMER.

WHAT CAN I DO FOR YOU, DR WEBB?

BALANCE THE WHEELS PLEASE, MITCHELL.

CERTAINLY, DOCTOR.

WHAT A ROBDOG! I WONDER IF HE'S BUMPED UP HIS PRICES FOR WHEEL BALANCING AS WELL. IT WOULDN'T SURPRISE ME.

THERE YOU GO, DOCTOR, ALL DONE. NO CHARGE AS USUAL.

THANK YOU, MITCHELL.

WHAT!?! THAT'S NOT FAIR.

SHORTLY.

THAT'S LUCKY, SILVER. MRS QUINTRELL SAID THIS IS THE LAST TOILET ROLL IN THE VILLAGE. APPARENTLY EVERYBODY HAS BEEN RUNNING OUT UNEXPECTEDLY.

NO DOGS, EXCEPT GUIDE DOGS AND BOY DETECTIVE CANINE SIDEKICKS.

WE'D BETTER GET BACK. IT'S NEARLY TIME FOR MEG'S AFTERNOON DUTY.

THERE'LL BE HELL TO PAY IF SHE HAS TO WIPE HER NICK ON THE CARDBOARD AGAIN.

WOOF!

JACK LOST NO TIME IN GETTING HOME.

THANK GOODNESS YOU'RE BACK. I'VE GOT A RIGHT OLD TURTLE'S HEAD AND NO MISTAKE.

YOU GO AND HAVE A SIT ON THIS, WHILE I GO AND PUT THE NEW TOILET ROLL ON THE HOLDER.

SO...

THERE! LET'S GIVE AUNT MEG A SHOUT.

AUNT MEG! YOU CAN COME UP AND DROP YOUR COPPER BOLT NOW!

OH THANK YOU, JACK. JUST IN TIME TOO. THE DETONATOR'S GONE OFF.

WELL DON'T WORRY. I'VE PUT A FRESH ROLL ON THE...

EH!?! WHERE DID IT GO?

WHAT IS IT, BOY? WHAT HAVE YOU SEEN.

WOOF!

WOOF!

WOOF!

WHY, THAT'S DR WEBB'S CAR. WHAT WAS HE DOING OUT THERE? THIS IS ALL VERY ODD.

KPH3C

EVERYBODY IN THE VILLAGE HAS PILES...MITCHELL IS BUMPING UP HIS INNER TUBE PRICES...TOILET ROLLS ARE GOING MISSING...AND DR WEBB GETS HIS WHEELS BALANCED FOR NOTHING. THERE'S A MYSTERY GOING ON, SILVER, AND I RECKON DR WEBB IS AT THE BOTTOM OF IT!

EARLY NEXT MORNING.

LOOK, SILVER. HE'S LOADING SOMETHING INTO HIS CAR. LET'S FOLLOW HIM AND SEE WHAT HE'S UP TO.

KPH3C

COME ON, BOY. WE MUSN'T LET HIM GET AWAY.

SOON.

THERE HE IS, OUTSIDE OLD GRANNY MIGGIN'S HOUSE. HE SEEMS TO BE TAKING A TENT OF SOME SORT OUT OF THE BOOT.

IT'S A WORKMAN'S TENT. I WONDER WHAT HE'S DOING IN THERE.

THERE'S ONLY ONE WAY TO FIND OUT.

117

CONTINUED OVER

AS QUIETLY AS THEY COULD, JACK AND SILVER CREPT UP TO SEE WHAT SINISTER HAPPENINGS WERE TAKING PLACE IN THE WORKMAN'S TENT.

SO THAT'S HIS GAME!

HE'S USING HIS REMOTE SURGICAL OPERATING TOOLS TO GRAB PEOPLE'S TOILET PAPER AND PULL IT THROUGH THE SEWERS INTO HIS TENT.

BUT WHY, JACK?

I THINK I KNOW THE ANSWER TO THAT, BUT WE WON'T FIND IT HERE. COME ON BOY, LET'S GO AND SEE PC BROWN.

LATER THAT DAY.

AH, DR WEBB. WHAT CAN I DO FOR YOU TODAY?

BALANCE MY TYRES AGAIN, WOULD YOU, MITCHELL.

HOLD IT RIGHT THERE! PC BROWN! ARREST THOSE TWO!

OF COURSE, JACK...

EH!?!

WHAT THE...!?!

...BUT COULD YOU EXPLAIN WHY?

WITH PLEASURE. DR WEBB HAS BEEN BORROWING THE HOSPITAL'S REMOTE CONTROL EQUIPMENT. UNDER COVER OF A WORKMAN'S TENT, HE SENDS THE ROBOT ARMS DOWN THE SEWERS AND UP THROUGH PEOPLE'S TOILETS.

THERE, HE GRABS THEIR TOILET ROLL AND PULLS IT DOWN THROUGH THE SEWERS AND INTO HIS TENT.

BUT WHAT WOULD WEBB WANT WITH TOILET PAPER THAT'S BEEN DRAGGED THROUGH THE SEWER?

NOTHING, BUT THEN THE UNLUCKY HOUSEHOLDERS ARE FORCED TO WIPE THEIR BOTTOMS WITH THE CARDBOARD TUBE. AFTER SEVERAL DAYS OF THIS...

THEY INVARIABLY DEVELOP AGONISING PILES...

PILES SO PAINFUL THEY ARE FORCED TO SIT ON AN INNER TUBE FOR COMFORT. AND NO PRIZES FOR GUESSING WHO SELLS THE POOR WRETCHES THESE INNER TUBES...AT AN INFLATED PRICE, IF YOU'LL FORGIVE THE PUN.

I CAN SEE HOW MITCHELL PROFITS FROM PEOPLE'S PILES, BUT WHY WOULD DR WEBB STEAL BOG ROLL IN THE FIRST PLACE? WHAT'S IN IT FOR HIM?

SIMPLE. IN RETURN FOR GIVING PEOPLE CHALFONTS...

...AND INCREASING MITCHELL'S SALES OF INNER TUBES, WEBB GETS HIS WHEELS BALANCED FOR FREE...AND AT £5 A TIME, THAT SOON ADDS UP. CAN I PUT THE HANDCUFFS ON THEM, PC BROWN?

I DON'T LIKE TO TELL YOU THIS, JACK, BUT I CAN'T ARREST THEM.

WHAT!?!

THEY MAY HAVE BEHAVED ABOMINABLY, BUT NO CRIME HAS BEEN COMMITTED.

NO CRIME?

DR WEBB DID NOT PHYSICALLY ENTER THE HOUSES, AND BY THE TIME HE GOT THE TOILET PAPER THROUGH THE SOIL PIPE IT WAS WORTHLESS...

...SO NO THEFT HAD TAKEN PLACE.

BUT...

AS FOR MITCHELL...WELL, THIS IS A FREE MARKET. HE CAN CHARGE WHAT HE LIKES FOR HIS INNER TUBES, EVEN IF IT IS PROFITING FROM OTHER PEOPLE'S MISERY.

SO YOU MEAN...?

YES, JACK, I'M AFRAID SO...

...THEY WALK.

HEH! HEH! BETTER LUCK NEXT TIME, KID.

WHY YOU...!

LEAVE IT, JACK...LEAVE IT.

THAT NIGHT.

DON'T TAKE IT PERSONALLY, JACK. YOU KNOW IN THIS GAME THE GOOD GUYS DON'T ALWAYS COME OUT ON TOP. SOME YOU WIN, SOME YOU LOSE.

S'JUSS NO' FAIR.

LIFE AIN'T FAIR. ANYONE TELLS YOU OTHERWISE IS A JACKASS.

BUT THEY'LL MAKE A MISTAKE ONE DAY. WISE GUYS LIKE THEM ALWAYS DO...AND WHEN THEY DO...

...WE'LL BE WAITING TO BUST THEIR ASS!

118

THE END

Britain 'Nearly Finished' say Builders

THE BRICKS AND MORTAR are almost done and the plaster is all but dry. Because, according to the country's construction industry, Britain is nearly finished.

"We've got a year or two to go, no more," smiles Dave Davids, clerk of works at some building site or other.

"There's just a bit of the A12 near Felixstowe needs doing, and a development of luxury flats in Leeds to finish, and then it's all over, and people can start enjoying the place properly."

Impending

But feelings about the impending ending of the massive 14,000-year project are mixed.

"I'm out of a job when this is finished," says tiler Steve Stevens. "I suppose I'll have to re-train as a management consultant or go around robbing old ladies or something."

And sceptics say the end is not nearly as nigh as optimists would have people believe.

"We all know there's going to be snagging," says Geoff Geoffreys of BuilderWatch UK. "And 1-2 years means 6-8 builder years."

"You know what they're like. They'll start the job, then they'll be off working on 2 or 3 other countries as well. I wouldn't be surprised if Britain wasn't finished until long after the Olympics have packed up and gone home."

LETTERBOCKS

Viz Comic, PO Box 656
North Shields NE26 1BT
e-mail: letters@viz.co.uk

★ STAR ★ LETTER ★

When I was a girl, we would always spend our holidays each year in Mablethorpe. We passed our days playing in the sun on the beach, paddling in the sea and catching crabs on the pier. So, when I opened my paper the other day and read an horrific story about a man who was anally raped and stabbed by a gang of Norwegian bikers and left for dead in a public toilet on Mablethorpe seafront, it brought all those lovely childhood memories flooding back.

Edna Hucknall, Nottingham

I saw Jay Kay being interviewed on *Top Gear* the other day, and he came over as a complete cunt. How he managed to look like a complete cunt at the side of Jeremy Clarkson is anybody's guess, but the cunt managed it somehow.

Frank Whittle, Leicester

Congratulations to the BBC on their marvellous coverage of the Beijing Olympic Games. Sixteen days and not one of the presenters used the word inscrutable. Mind you, having said that they did start every programme with that plinky-plonky music they always play.

T Harbottle, Tring

mr. LOGIC

I spotted a sign outside a school the other day that read 'Parking here could cost a child's life.' I think that seems a little severe. Surely a fine would be enough, or perhaps a couple of points on your licence.

A Crombie, Dudley

I was a little disappointed to see that last Sunday's London Olympic handover party was sponsored by Visa. Presumably this means that it was all on tick. If we couldn't afford to hold the party, we shouldn't have got it on the never never.

T Hertabuis, North Lake

What's happened to pygmies? Why don't we hear about pygmies any more? Come on, the BBC - bring back programmes about pygmies.

J Harding, Robertsbridge

They say that breast feeding is healthy and natural, and that a woman should be able to do it anywhere. I agree, but I would like to point out that masturbation is also healthy and natural, not that you'd think it with the reaction I got on the number 14 bus this morning.

Mike Wakefield, e-mail

Whilst I enjoyed the Olympics, I did notice that there weren't any large breasted women in any of the events. Come on big-jugged girls, get on the treadmill and let's see you in 2012.

Norman Fletcher, e-mail

The other day I was terrified when I saw what I thought was a lion in our local park. Fortunately it turned out to be just a very large puma that had escaped from the zoo.

H Sputnik, Cardiff

I'm tired of hearing that the NHS doesn't have enough money for any more beds. Now I'm not very good at maths, but with an annual budget of £90 billion, that's surely enough to buy a bed for everyone in Britain. You can get them from MFI for £89.99 each.

Darren Conway, e-mail

I thought you might be interested in this picture from our local ice-cream van. I assume it's supposed to be Winnie the Pooh and Tweetypie, but fuck me it's shit even by *Viz* standards. Have any readers seen a worse representation of a cartoon figure used for advertising frozen dairy confectionary?

Simon Pearce, e-mail

p.s. You should see Sylvester, he looks like he's got AIDs.

They say romance is dead, do they? Well I don't think I've ever heard anyone say 'romance is dead', except as part of the phrase 'and they say romance is dead.'

Chris Caif, e-mail

Scientists claim that the Big Bang was the loudest noise that has ever occured in history, They obviously haven't been in the same room as my grandma when she's watching telly.

Jonathan Wright, e-mail

It seems a little short-sighted of the authorities to release Gary Glitter from prison early for good behaviour. He is a child molester and there are no children in prison. Presumably it was very easy for him to behave himself whilst behind bars.

Chris Lou, e-mail

In 1998 a monkey in Gibraltar felt my wife's tit and ran away. Dirty little bastard.

Craig Eddie, e-mail

Jesus said unto his disciples, "Follow me." However, in the Garden of Gethsemane, he said, "Stay here." Frankly, I don't know what to believe anymore.

Father Ted O'Meara, e-mail

I moved house recently and decided to redecorate the bedroom. In order to do the job properly, I moved the radiator and was appalled to discover a pair of the previous owner's underwear down the back. Then I suddenly remembered that I had bought the house off Keira Knightly. Any offers?

H Rumblefish, Luton

DOCTORS. Take a tip from Search for a Star shows like *Any Dream Will Do* to make your patients' hospital visits more exciting. Say "And the results of your cancer tests are..." then leave a two minute silence to build up the tension.

H Moron, Luton

ANARCHISTS. When smashing the state, take care not to burn down your dole office.

Charles Palmer, e-mail

A GLASS mixing bowl turned upside down over a saucer of water in the garden makes an ideal Centre Parcs for ants.

Mike, e-mail

ACTORS. Improve your chances of landing a role in a Tim Burton film by being Helena Bonham-Carter.

Ted Bartlett, e-mail

UTILITY companies. Encourage customers to go to 'paperless billing' and online account management to help the environment. It has the added benefit of rendering them helpless when you overcharge them as they have no bills to check through and your computer can 'mysteriously freeze their on-line account.' It makes it almost impossible for them to prove you are a bunch of robbing bastards.

Jay, e-mail

BRITISH Airways. Next time you run out of breakfasts mid-way through serving a Montreal to Heathrow flight, why not just admit it, instead of mumbling stuff about "we're just waiting to find something" before serving half the plane three dry bread rolls and a fucking bar of chocolate?

A Rugby, Newcastle

HUSBANDS. Cheer yourself up by watching your wedding video in reverse. You'll love the bit where you give her back the ring, walk back up the aisle, get into a car and fuck off.

Ben Nicol, Mernda

DEATH ROW prisoners. Increase your life span by a few days by having your last meal delivered from Pizza Hut.

Grant B Warner, New Malden

Aren't Men Daft!!?

I SENT MY boyfriend to the shops for a loaf of bread and a pint of milk. When he came back, he'd remembered the bread but forgotten the milk!

Gloria Prepuce, Jarrow

TALK ABOUT dippy, my hubbie must take the biscuit. He suffered a massive head injury whilst working on an oil rig six years ago, and has been in a persistent vegetative state ever since. The silly sausage doesn't even know what day it is!

Noreen Glanshood, Yeovil

MY HUSBAND's daft as a brush. I went round to my neighbour's house and found him stark naked in bed on top of her. The daft 'ap'orth had gone into the wrong house and climbed into bed with the wrong woman! I ask you!

Janice Foreskin, Hull

Are They Still Dead?

I USED TO love the comedian **Bernie Winters**, especially when he appeared with his dog Schnorbitz. I know he passed on a few years ago, but I couldn't help wondering if he was still dead?

Dean, e-mail

★ Born Bernard Weinstein on September 6th 1932, Bernie Winters was a regular on our screens with his brother Mike for many years. He died on May 4th 1991. A quick phonecall to his ex agent reveals that Bernie is indeed still dead and has no plans to come to life in the immediate future.

COULD YOU tell me if the 60s singer **Janis Joplin** is still dead? I used to love her songs and it would be great to see her live in concert.

Franklyn Mint, Suffolk

★ I'm afraid you won't be seeing her anytime soon, Mr Mint. The hard-drinking rock wildchild died on October 4th 1970, and a quick check with Los Angeles Crematorium authorities reveal that as of yesterday she was still dead. "I've just had the lid off for a look and Janice's ashes are still in their urn", cemetery owner Hyman Prepuce told us.

I WAS WATCHING a film where an ancient Egyptian mummy came back to life and went round strangling people. It set me wondering, has the famous mummified pharoah **Tutankhamun** ever come back to life, and if so, did he go round strangling people?

Dr M Baker, Haltwhistle

★ Tutankhamun, son-in-law of Akhenaten died at the age of 18 in 1340BC and his tomb lay undiscovered until 1922. On his death, his organs were removed and put into canopic jars and his brain was pulled down through his nose with a big hook, so it is unlikely that he ever came back to life. However, a British Museum spokesman confirms that there was a curse found on his tomb, so he could not rule out the possibility that the boy king's bandaged corpse could come back to life at some point to wreak terrible revenge on those who disturbed his eternal slumber.

WE WERE saddened to hear of the death of Australian naturalist **Steve Irwin** after he was stang off a fish. My family was wondering if he is still dead, or whether he has any plans to appear on our screens again.

T Coatzee, Luton

★ Crocodile hunter Steve, with his catchphrase 'Oh, Crikey', brought the world of Australian wildlife into millions of homes. However, he is presently in a wooden box under six feet of earth at Australia Zoo, and has no current plans to return to television presenting.

MY MOTHER used to adore the actress **Noele Gordon** who died a long time ago. I wonder if you could tell me what she is doing now, or is she still dead?

Maurice Micklewhite, e-mail

★ Noele Gordon, or Nolly to her fans, appeared in over 6000 episodes of Crossroads in the 60s and 70s. She passed away on April 14th 1985 and has been dead ever since. However, a true professional, the late Noele still works tirelessly and this Christmas is appearing in Aladdin at the Hull Empire.

ROBIN HOOD & HIS MARRIED MEN

PAUL PALMER VIZ 08

WHAT SAY YOU WE STORM THE SHERIFF'S CASTLE AND STEAL HIS GOLD, MEN?

THIS AFTERNOON? GOSH, THAT'S A BIT AWKWARD. IT'S MY TURN TO PICK UP THE KIDS!

I'M GOING FOOD SHOPPING WITH THE WIFE.

SORRY, ROBIN, I'VE GOT THE IN-LAWS ROUND!

PLAYTIME FONTAYNE

MR. BURKETT IS HERE TO SEE YOU, MR. FONTAYNE.

SEND HIM IN, PLEASE, MISS FAIRCLOUGH.

TAKE A SEAT, MR. BURKETT... NOW, HOW CAN I BE OF ASSISTANCE?

IT'S ABOUT MY COMPANY OVERDRAFT, MR. FONTAYNE.

AS YOU MAY KNOW, BURKETT'S DARTS LTD'S SALES HAVE BEEN HIT QUITE BADLY BY THE RECENT DOWNTURN...

SEVERAL OF OUR BIG WHOLE-SALE CUSTOMERS HAVE GONE BUST OWING US LARGE AMOUNTS OF MONEY...

MEANWHILE, OUR OVERHEADS HAVE INCREASED BY FORTY PERCENT YEAR-ON-YEAR...

TRANSPORT COSTS, UTILITIES AND THE RENTAL OF OUR BUSINESS PREMISES HAVE ALL SEEN SUBSTANTIAL HIKES...

OUR SUPPLIERS ARE PUTTING THEIR PRICES UP TOO.

WE'VE GOT A BIG ORDER COMING IN FEBRUARY THAT WILL PUT US BACK ON OUR FEET... BUT MEANWHILE, WE HAVE URGENT BILLS THAT NEED PAYING RIGHT NOW.

IF WE CAN'T IMPROVE OUR CASHFLOW, WE'LL HAVE TO CLOSE THE FACTORY AND MAKE 24 PEOPLE REDUNDANT WHICH WOULD BE AWFUL SO CLOSE TO CHRISTMAS...

IDEALLY, MR. FONTAYNE, WE'D LIKE TO DOUBLE OUR PRESENT BUSINESS OVERDRAFT FACILITY IN ORDER TO TIDE US OVER THE NEXT COUPLE OF MONTHS.

RIGHT...

WELL, LET'S SEE WHAT WE CAN DO, SHALL WE.? WHAT SORT OF MAXIMUM REPAYMENT TERM WOULD YOU BE LOOKING AT, MR. BURKETT?

SIX MONTHS?

SIX... I SEE...

ONE...TWO...THREE...FOUR...FIVE... SIX!

...AT, SAY, OUR USUAL NOMINAL HALF-YEARLY COMPOUND RATE OF 8%...

...ONE...TWO...THREE...FOUR...FIVE...SIX...SEVEN...EIGHT!

BUT MR. FONTAYNE, THIS IS HARDLY...

PICK A COLOUR.

...ER...BLUE?

B...L...U...E!

OPEN THAT AND READ WHAT IT SAYS.

"THE BANK REGRETS TO INFORM YOU THAT ON THIS OCCASION IT HAS NOT BEEN POSSIBLE TO PROCEED WITH YOUR REQUEST FOR A TEMPORARY EXTENSION TO YOUR COMPANY'S OVERDRAFT FACILITY"

ALL OF IT! READ OUT ALL OF IT!

...AND I SMELL OF POO.

HAAR! HAAR! MR. BURKETT SMELLS OF POO! HAAR! HAAR! TSSSSS!

I HEARD HIM! HE SAID IT!

123

THE verdict of Lord Justice Scott Baker's inquest has done little to silence speculation about the true causes of Princess Diana's death in 1997.

Now the case files have been closed and the blame for her assassination has been placed squarely at the door of drunken driver Henri Paul and the chasing Paris paparazzi pack. Yet surveys suggest that up to more than a third of the British public still believes that the Princess of Hearts was deliberately killed in a staged accident. These people, including Mohamed Al-Fayed, everyone who writes for or reads the *Daily Express* and Keith Allen, are certain that it was Prince Philip who was behind the dastardly plot.

ENCOUNTER

However, in his summing up the judge cleared the Duke of Edinburgh of any involvement

in Diana's death due to a lack of evidence. The Prince's perfect murder plot to run Di's car off the road in Paris's Pont de l'Alma tunnel using motorcycling photographers, a white Fiat Uno, no seatbelts and a pissed-up chauffeur would have taken years to plan, required meticulous, split-second timing to pull off successfully, and required a cover-up on a scale to rival NASA's faked Moon landings.

PANT

It would also have entailed a massive conspiracy involving royals, photographers, secret services, French police, paramedics, Paris Ritz staff, BBC reporters, diplomats and hundreds of other witnesses in order to succeed. Surely there must have been a simpler way for the establishment to get rid

PRINCESS

How the Stars Would of Pulled

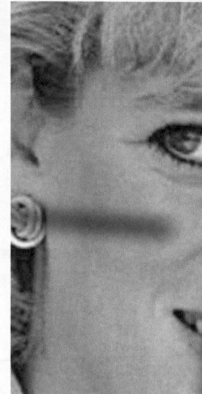

PERFECT MURDER NUMBER ONE

JAMIE OLIVER IN THE RESTAURANT WITH A LAMB SHANK

Naked Chef Jamie could have easily cooked up a pukka way to assassinate England's Rose. He would have invited her to his exclusive restaurant - Fifteen - where he would have shown her to a secluded private booth on the pretext of allowing her to escape from her press pursuers. Then, while she was looking at the menu, Oliver would have sneaked in through a serving hatch and clubbed her repeatedly on the back of the head with a frozen leg of lamb. Then he would have calmly returned to the kitchen and started cooking the murder weapon, drizzling it with extra virgin olive oil, cracked peppercorns and sprigs of fresh rosemary, before slamming it into a medium oven for twenty minutes per pound, not forgetting to baste it half way

through. Lovely jubbly.

Sooner or later, one of the customers would have spotted Diana's blood-soaked corpse slumped across the table and raised the alarm. Then, when the police arrived Jamie would have helped them with their enquiries, before calmly bringing out the delicious-smelling cooked lamb and offering it to them to eat, saying it would be a shame to waste it.

As they tucked into their delicious freebie meal of braised lamb shank, celeriac mash and glazed shallots, little would the unsuspecting cops have realised that they were actually destroying the only piece of forensic evidence that could link their generous, big-tongued host to the killing. Bish-bosh-bash on the head....sorted!

PERFECT MURDER NUMBER TWO

NOEL EDMONDS AT CRINKLEY BOTTOM WITH AN ACID-FILLED PIE

People might think that the tidy-bearded ex-*Late Late Breakfast Show* host could just have asked the Princess to do a Whirly Wheel Challenge or shot her in the face with his elephant gun. However, if he'd chosen to take her out in such an obvious way, the trail of blame would have led back to him too easily.

How he'd actually have done it is like this: Edmonds would have organised a charity event at his palatial Devon estate, giving helicopter rides to spastics or something, and invited Lady Diana to mark the occasion by unveiling a giant gold plaque in his honour. Just as his honoured guest was about to pull the cord, Noel would have had his old nemesis Mr Blobby step forward and "gunge" her with a giant custard pie. The Princess was such a down-to-earth, fun-loving lady that it was a racing certainty she would have pushed her security men aside so she could take the pie on her chin.

This would have been her big mistake, as sneaky Noel would have earlier swap-shopped the custard pie for one filled with deadly concentrated prussic acid. This would have dissolved her head off in seconds, killing her instantly. Edmonds would have pretended to be really shocked, knowing that no-one would have pointed the finger of blame at him because he is so well known for his extensive charity work.

The *Deal Or No Deal* presenter would have taken no chances; he would have made sure that the patsy in the Mr Blobby suit was a gullible halfwit who was unable to defend himself. And just to make 100% sure he couldn't be implicated in the plot, Noel would probably have had his friend Mike Smith step forward and shoot Blobby in an underground car park as he was transferred between two police stations a couple of days later.

PERFECT MURDE

THE KRANKIES ON A WALKA

The veteran Scotch comedy double-act would have had a fandabidozy chance of pulling off the perfect murder.

For obvious security reasons, members of the public were often kept at a distance from Lady Di. However, from her earliest days as a kindergarten teacher she was as well known for her love of children as she was for her love of standing with her back to the sun so you could see her fanny through her skirt if you really squinted. If, whilst on one of her many public engagements, she had been approached by a tiny schoolboy carrying a bunch of flowers, it is quite likely that her bodyguards would have let him through their tight cordon.

However, this would have been a

S MUST DI
Off the Crime of the Century

PERFECT MURDER NUMBER FOUR

JEREMY CLARKSON AT THE TOP GEAR TEST TRACK WITH A REASONABLY-PRICED CAR

Princess Diana was well known for being fiercely competitive. So if petrolhead TV presenter Jeremy Clarkson had invited her to take part in the "Star in a Reasonably-Priced Car" segment of his popular *Top Gear* programme, it is likely that the feisty Royal would have jumped at the chance to prove her mettle behind the wheel. Even more so if she had been told that her boot-faced love rival Camilla Parker-Bowles had been on the previous week's show, and had set a new *Top Gear* circuit record.

However, before Di began her timed lap, murderous Clarkson would have given the Stig twenty pounds to go out and sever the car's brake cables and loosen the steering wheel so that it would come off at high speed. Then, as the cameras rolled and she reached the fastest part of the track - out of the Hammerhead and into the Follow-Through - Di would have found her Chevrolet Lacetti out of control and unable to stop. Careering off the tarmac and somersaulting end over end, the curly-topped presenter's hapless royal victim would have perished in a fiery ball of twisted metal before help could arrive.

After the "accident", the motormouth presenter would have been able to relax safe in the knowledge that his famously-silent, helmeted accomplice would never tell the police what his boss had paid him to do to Diana's car. When questioned by police, Clarkson wouldn't break a sweat. Indeed, he would remain cool enough to be included on the famously dull and self-indulgent "Cool Wall" section of his own programme!

of the maverick Princess who was threatening to become an embarrassment to the Royal family.

MILK WOOD

These days, it seems we can't put on the television without seeing some show in which competing celebrities perform unaccustomed tasks such as ice skating, circus acrobatics or ballroom dancing. So how would the STARS have fared if they'd been called upon to commit the perfect crime? Just for fun, we asked celebrity criminologist Professor Greuze Brughwell to dream up a few ways in which A-List Stars might have dialled M for Murder.

Professor GREUZE BRUGHWELL is head of the Celebrity Criminology Department at the University of Loughborough. His new book 'SWITHLAND in old photographs' *(Vanity Books, £18.99)* is available in all good 24-hour garages in the immediate vicinity of Barrow-upon-Soar and his sister's sweet shop in Shepshed.

NUMBER THREE

... WITH AN ABATTOIR BOLTGUN

mistake, for the "schoolboy" would actually have been octogenarian actress Jeanette Krankie, and her tempting bouquet would have concealed a stolen slaughterhouse boltgun, powered by a canister of compressed gas hidden in her satchel. As an unsuspecting Di bent to smell the flowers, Krankie could have lifted the gun to the Princess's temple and pulled the trigger, punching a retractable metal bolt deep into her brain and killing her on the spot.

In the stunned, horrified silence which followed the hit, the tiny assassin would have taken the opportunity to make her escape, slipping easily through the legs of the crowd to a waiting getaway car driven by her husband/brother Ian.

PERFECT MURDER NUMBER FIVE

ROLF HARRIS IN THE ARTIST'S STUDIO WITH HIS DIDGERIDOO

The multi-talentless Australian is famous for his recent portrait of the Queen with the eyes and the mouth a bit wrong. And the chin and the teeth. As part of his assassination plan, Rolf would have used his many contacts at the BBC and Buckingham Palace to secure himself yet another commission - this time one to paint a portrait of Diana. And the arms.

Arriving at his light and airy studio, the unsuspecting Princess would have found herself seated by an open window in front of Harris's easel whilst the bearded entertainer busied himself behind the canvas. However, after sloshing brightly-coloured paint around with wallpaper paste brushes and decorator's rollers for a while, Rolf would have announced that he felt his sitter was looking a little tense, and this was making it even more difficult than usual for him to get a likeness.

To counteract this, Harris would then have suggested that he could help Di to relax by performing a live version of his hit Sun Arise, which reached number 3 in the 1962 Christmas pop chart. To this end, he would have produced his didgeridoo, taken a series of noisy deep breaths and raised it to his lips.

However, instead of the trademark spluttery, buzzing drone the Princess was expecting to come out the end of it, a poisoned dart would have emerged instead, sticking straight into her carotid artery and killing her in an instant. Painting her portrait would have given the bearded TV favourite the perfect opportunity to didgeri"doo" in the Princess. And what's more, Rolf's brilliant murder plot would have been so perfect that his victim wouldn't have known what it was yet until it was too late to save herself!

126

Quentin's CRISPS

I WAS a promising semi-professional footballer who had never even tried a crisp until 1995, when Gary Lineker started advertising them on the television. Because Gary was my sporting hero, I started to eat them by the box-full. 14 years down the line, I now weigh over 50-stone and suffer from scurvy, ulcerative colitis and congestive heart failure. How ironic that they are called Walker's Crisps, when I am unable to walk; I can't even turn over in my shit-filled bed.

Big Joe, Bradford

My Best Crisps!

Shakin' Stevens - *Salt'n'Shake*

I SENT my son out to buy me some Pringles at the corner shop. I couldn't believe my ears when he came back and told me he had just taken out a majority shareholding in the Scottish Borders-based knitwear manufacturers.

Mrs D Estelle, Falmouth

WITH reference to Mrs Estelle's letter *(above)*, the other day I needed some new diamond-patterned sweaters, so I sent my son out to buy me some Pringles. Imagine my shock when he came back with a cardboard tube containing overpriced crisps!

Val Doonican, Surrey

I AM an American, and during a recent holiday in England I went into a shop and asked for a bag of potato chips. Imagine my consternation when, instead of the crisps I was expecting, I was handed a ... no, hang on. This doesn't work.

Rhoda Felchenstein, New Jersey

I'M A huge crisps fan, so I got very excited the other day when I noticed that my local greengrocer was selling "Crispy Lettuces" at half price. But what a disappointment they turned out to be. They were large, green, soggy leaf-like things, and I had to empty nearly half a pound of salt and nearly a pint of vinegar onto them before they tasted anything like crisps. I certainly shan't be buying any of those again!

Emma Outhwaite, York

"Hi, Crispophiles! Caroline Quentin here. I've had a really big bag this week... crisps, that is! Yum yum! But enough about my crisps, it's time for some letters about yours!"

DURING the war, when rationing was on, my mother used to make her own crisps. She used to fix a potato in my dad's workbench vice and use his carpentry plane to shave off crisp-sized slivers. Then she used to iron the slices individually, flavouring them with dried bacon rind and onion skins, then leave them in the airing cupboard to cool down. Finally, she would unpick an old jumper and use the wool to knit a crisp bag to keep them in. In the 60 years since the end of the war, I have eaten many bags of so-called "proper" crisps, and do you know, I've never tasted anything even remotely as disgusting as my mother's home-made versions.

Phyllis Crabs, Manchester

I AM an American, and during a recent holiday in England I went into a shop and asked for a bag of French fries. Imagine my consternation when, instead of the ... no. It's still wrong.

Rhoda Felchenstein, New Jersey

AS A Professor of English Literature, I am constantly disgusted by crisp manufacturers who insist on replacing the "and" in "salt and vinegar" with a "'n'". And the phrase "Ready Salted" similarly leaves me incensed. The word "Ready" is an adjective, not an adverb. It is a simple grammatical fact that an adjective cannot be used to qualify the word "salted". With such poor standards of literacy on crisp bags, is it any wonder that this country is going to hell in a handcart?

Prof. A Gowans-Whyte, Cambridge

I AGREE with Professor Gowans-Whyte *(letter, above)*. Crisp manufacturers are setting a very poor example when it comes to the standard of English used on their packaging. We should not be expected to put up with it. To this end, when I go into my local corner shop, I refuse to hand over my hard-earned money for "Wotsits". Instead, I make a point of asking for a bag of "Which Are Theys".

Dr O Trubshaw, Carshalton

MY CAT Mr Truffles loves crisps. I took a photograph of him the other day with his paw stuck in a bag of his favourite Cheese & Onion crisps, and all crumbs in his whiskers. However, I'll not get round to finishing the film off until my summer holidays, so here's a photograph of my late sister instead.

Mrs Hilda Feldman, Jarrow

My Best Crisps!

Rose West - *Salt & Vinegar Chipstix*

Crispy Laffs

Q: *What sort of crisps do musicians like?*
A: Quavers.
Mrs Edna Arteriosclerosis, Glasgow

Q: *What sort of crisps do chiropodists like?*
A: Cheese and bunion.
Mrs Edna Arteriosclerosis, Glasgow

Q: *What sort of crisps do you call a sailor with a bottle of vinegar?*
A: Salt and Vinegar.
Mrs Doreen Angina, Glasgow

Q: *What other sort of crisps do chiropodists like?*
A: Pickled bunion.
Mrs Edna Arteriosclerosis, Glasgow

Readers' Crisps

C. Harris, St Leonards

Caroline's Crisp Bag

YOUR CRISP PROBLEMS SOLVED

Dear Caroline,
DURING a recent holiday in Dorset, my wife and I shared a particularly delicious bag of Walker's crisps which we bought from a shop in Corfe Castle. Foolishly, we threw the bag away when we had finished the crisps, so we have no idea what the flavour was. It was a green bag and we would love to find out the flavour of the crisps so we could buy another one.
T Medford, Cricklewood

When I got your letter, I chartered an executive jet and flew to the Leicestershire headquarters of Walker's Crisps, where I had a meeting with Sir Giles Walker, the company founder. Sadly, he is now in his late 90s and was unable to remember which varieties of his firm's products come in green bags, but thought that the ones you ate in Devon could possibly have been Cheese & Onion or Smoky Bacon.

Send in your crisp-related queries to: Quentin's Crisps, c/o Viz, PO Box 656, North Shields NE30 4XX. There's a crisp bag of barbeque beef crisps for every problem that we use.

Your Little Blue Salt Bag Texts

litl blu salt bag rox 100%! crispy_jim, leeds

Y DO I HAV 2 PUT MI OWN SALT ON MI *&£*@ING CRISPS? WOTA RIPOF! ANTIBAG DAVE

jim of leeds get a life salt bags R 4 losers_gurrl_

GURRL IS TH REAL LOSER.SALT BAGS R WKD!DR_FRANCIS_WHITLEYBAY

antibag dave is gay_ the bagmeister

fuk of bagmeister im not gay u r u cunt frm antibag dave

antibag dave ur mum just sukd me of!!!_the bagmeister

Y R THEY BLU?WOTS RONG WIV RED

FOR US MANU FANS?ROONEY4EVA

BAGMEISTER U R FUKIN DED FRM ANTIBAG DAVE

Hi. Does anyone know when the little blue salt bag was invented? George

GEORGE U TAKIN TH FUKIN PISS OR WOT?U R DED 2 FRM ANTIBAG DAVE

nice1 rooney4eva! league facup championsleague champnions1999! ronaldofan

manu shit wankers fuk of u pedos_dennis hopkins from wimbledon

I just fucked Antibag Dave's mum up the arse. George

Kids Say the Funniest Things about Crisps

MY HUSBAND and I recently took our six-year-old grandson to a local Indian restaurant as a birthday treat. "Look nana!" he announced at the top of his voice as we sat down at our table. "Those are the biggest crisps I have ever seen!" Needless to say, he was looking at a plate of poppadoms! It still reduces me and my husband to helpless tears of hysterical laughter for several hours every time we think about it.

Mrs Glenda Feverish, Hull

MY WIFE is horribly afflicted with septic psoriasis, like the character played by Michael Gambon in *The Singing Detective*. The other day, she had just been scratching her face and scalp and was brushing a large pile of dry skin flakes off the table into a dustpan when our four-year-old grandson came into the kitchen. "Gosh granny," he piped up. "Those are the smallest crisps I have ever seen!"

Bert Mills, Essex

My Best Crisps!

Richard Gere - *Beef Space Raiders*

OH, LORDY! IT'S THE FAT SLAGS

'ERE, TRAY...'AVE YOU BEEN BORROWIN' MY KNICKERS AGAIN?

NO

WELL, I'M MISSIN' SOME...

...FOUR PAIR OF ME BEST COMFIE ONES 'AVE GONE... I PUT 'EM IN 'ERE YESTERDAY MORNIN'...

HEY...'OLD ON!

I SAW BAZ GOIN' THROUGH Y'KNICKER DRAWER LAST NIGHT...

Y'NEVER!

AYE!

WOT, BAZ!? NAH! HE PROBABLY WANTS 'EM FOR WANKIN' INTO

THE DIRTY DOG!

NO... DON'T GET AT 'IM...

BEH! THE BIG PERV! D'Y'THINK HE'S A SECRET TRANNY, TRAY?

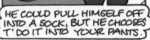

Y'SHOULD BE FLATTERED THAT YOU AN' YER UNDIES ARE PART OF 'IS MASTURBATORY FANTASIES

D' YOU THINK?

AYE!

HE COULD PULL HIMSELF OFF INTO A SOCK, BUT HE CHOOSES T'DO IT INTO YOUR PANTS.

YER RIGHT. D'Y'KNOW, I'M GOIN' T'NIP ROUND T'HIS PLACE AN' GIVE 'IM ONE...

...IT'LL BE A NICE SURPRISE FOR 'IM

SEE Y'IN A BIT, TRAY

2 MINS LATER...

THAT WERE QUICK, SAN

'AD HE ALREADY GONE OFF INTO 'EM?

SLAM!

NO... HE'S DECORATIN' HIS FRONT ROOM AN' HE'S USIN' 'EM AS FUCKIN' DUSTSHEETS!

NOBBY'S PILES

I'M DOING A CHARITY PARACHUTE JUMP TO RAISE MONEY FOR HAEMORRHOID RESEARCH...!

OKAY NOBBY! WE'RE RIGHT OVER THE DROP ZONE!

GERONIMO!

OH NO! I'M DRIFTING OFF COURSE!

FUCK MY LUCK! I BET I COME DOWN WITH MY BRASS-EYE ON THE SHARP END OF THAT CHURCH SPIRE...!

GNNN...!

SUDDEN FORTUITOUS GUST OF WIND

¿PHEW!¿

THAT WAS A CLOSE ONE!

OLYMPIC JAVELIN DELIVERIES Ltd.

BOER WAR MEMORIAL

WORLD'S LARGEST PENCIL SHARPENER

CAUTION! SKIP FULL OF BROKEN GLASS, INDUSTRIAL LATHE SWARF & ROCK SALT

FANS TURN SCREW ON BOULT

ANGRY MUSIC fans were last night calling for the sacking of conductor *Sir Adrian Boult* after the London Symphony Orchestra turned in another poor performance playing Schubert at the Festival Hall.

A crowd of 10,000 concertgoers watched the players give a lacklustre 1st half rendition of the 8th Symphony in D minor, and a stony-faced Boult was booed off the dais as he left the stage at the interval.

Insiders say the 58-year-old maestro gave the orchestra 'a proper roasting' in the dressing room. "He was absolutely furious with them," said one source. "I've been in the orchestra business for forty years and I've never seen a conductor lose it like that. He must of knew his job was on the line."

As the second half got underway, the orchestra began their rendition of Mozart's Requiem with more spirit than they had shown in the first half, and there was a feeling that the players had raised their game following Boult's hairdryer treatment at half time. But it wasn't long before the familiar silly mistakes began to creep back in. A fumble by the principal clarinettist during a slow movement led to the double basses missing a cue, and the angry cat-calls from the crowd began again.

Performance Leaves Conductor's Job on Line

BOULT: Is the maestro set for the nut-heap?

Shortly afterwards, a trombone set-piece was well off the pace, and left Boult throwing his baton to the ground in despair. When the audience members were finally put out of their misery, the orchestra left the stage to a chorus of angry boos and whistles. Several members tore up their LSO season tickets in disgust and threw them at Sir Adrian.

"This performance was unacceptable," fumed angry fan *Quentin Cuthbert,* who had travelled from Holland Park for the concert. *"Schubert's 8th should have been a walkover for players of this calibre. Instead, they played like a bloody school orchestra."*

As the crowd left the hall, there was no doubt who was being blamed for the poor performance.

"Boult played with four kettle drums at the back and only twelve principal violins. That left the bassoons wide open looking for their cues during the fast movements," raged Tarquin Bumboy. "What was he thinking of?"

And chairman of supporters' club *Friends of the LSO* Crispin Fortescue was equally disappointed. "I've followed the orchestra for years, and this is the worst I've ever seen them play," he said. "The violas were sloppy, the horn section was outclassed throughout, and the triangles simply weren't good enough. They simply weren't playing like an orchestra. It was a national embarrassment. Boult is the conductor and he has to take the rap."

The Trustees of the LSO were last night fending off an angry chorus of calls for Boult's dismissal. And although no official announcement has been made, it is thought it will not be long before they are forced to bow to public opinion and show Sir Adrian the door of the Royal Albert Hall.

LSO DEAR!
What Went Wrong on the Night

1st HALF	**14 MINUTES:** *Crash!* Cymbal comes in a semitone late during Scherzo movement.
1st HALF	**37 MINUTES:** *Bang!* Flute plays pianissimo during fortissimo overture.
2nd HALF	**88 MINUTES:** *Wallop!* Harp glissando set-piece goes tits up.

SHOCKER: How the Sun reported the concert

Drunken bakers

Giz ya booze or y'gonna git stabbed up innit?

Let's see the knife then.

click

Always worth checking.

Lucky it was only the three per cent crap.

Cooking lager...

Yeah, but all the same —

— you can't whack a can in the park of a morning.

Meanwhile

There's a lot to be said for your cheap spirit.

Pricewise...

They might *taste* shit but you still get the warmth inside.

What have you been up to then lads?

Oh, relaxing.

Bakery's dead...

Got some kids just over there saying you gave them ten cans of lager.

Sixteen.

No —

—we'd had six.

He's right.

Ten it was.

Okay, could you both stand up please?

I don't see why not.

Bll*aechk*k!

Do either of you boys like a bit of parkin?

Who is the Most Marvellous Mills?

WHETHER they're squabbling in the High Court over multi-million pound divorces or releasing new LPs of knockabout piano tunes, **HEATHER MILLS** and **MRS MILLS** are rarely out of the headlines. But which one is the best? It's an argument that is threatening to split the country into two warring factions. Perhaps you side with blonde beauty Heather - who has touched northern hearts with her selfless charity work. Or do you prefer late, overweight piano-thumper Mrs, whose tunes kept cockney knees in a perpetual state of elevation throughout the sixties and seventies?

Now it's time to settle this burgeoning civil war once and for all. Here, we weigh up the pros and cons of the two most famous Millses in the land in order to decide which one is our Mills of Hearts.

Heather v Mrs

Heather		Round		Mrs

Heather kicks off with a good score, as husbands don't come much more celebrity-er than mop-top ex-Fab Paul McCartney. Lovely Heather bagged herself the lonely-hearted Beatle after the two met at a landmine charity awards ceremony and she was instantly swept off her feet. Despite his Beatlemania heyday being way in the past, Macca still makes headline news wherever he goes.

8 — Celebrity Husbands — 5

Mrs gets off to a bad start as her husband of forty years, Mr Mills, failed to achieve any celebrity status of note during his life. The closest he got was in 1964, when he gained brief notoriety after he was accused of stealing a typewriter ribbon from the offices where he was employed as a lift attendant, and his picture appeared in the court section of the local paper. A low scoring round.

Before rising to fame as a charity fundraiser, vegetarian campaigner and writer, Heather Mills enjoyed a moderately successful career as a glamour model. She famously appeared in *Die Freuden der Liebe*, a prestigious German educational manual on human relationships, in which she was pictured smearing herself and her male co-educator with whipped cream and baby oil.

9 — Modelling Career — 5

Because of her busy recording schedule, Mrs Mills had no time to cultivate a career as a professional model. However, it is not out of the question that Mr Mills could have snapped the odd saucy polaroid of his wife reclining over the kitchen work surface wearing nothing but stockings and suspenders and a sequined eye-mask. These photos could possibly later have appeared in the Readers Wives section of *Razzle* or *Parade*, netting her lucky hubby a cool fiver for each one.

Heather is a long time campaigner for animal rights and a dedicated vegan, shunning sausages, bacon, pork pies and Scotch eggs. In fact, she is so committed to her beliefs that she even avoids dairy produce, and when she posed for a series of German educational photographs, she insisted that the cream she smeared around her breasts and nipples was synthetic.

9 — Animal Rights/ Vegetarianism — 3

Mrs cared little for the plight of animals, and her trademark honky-tonk upright piano boasted 88 ivory keys. What's more, so heavy was her playing style, (each arm weighing in at a hefty 14 stone) that the whole keyboard had to be replaced once a week. By the end of her career, it is estimated that Mrs had pounded her way through the tusks of no less than 6,000 elephants.

At times, the British media has treated publicity-shy Heather worse than a murderer or a paedophile, so it came as no surprise when the strain became too much for her. She eventually snapped during a live GMTV interview in 2007, when her voice went all high, a bit like Stan Laurel.

7 — TV Breakdowns — 3

A low scoring round for Mrs, whose sunny disposition was her trademark. Even when talking about upsetting experiences, such as her time in the blitz, her husband's death in the mechanism of an escalator, or the time she was mauled by a grizzly bear, she always kept smiling.

Heather is no stranger to the divorce courts. In 1991 she got divorced from her first husband, dishwasher salesman Alfie Karmal. Her second divorce, from ex-Beatle Paul McCartney, has so far lasted longer than her first marriage, but with one failed marriage under her belt and one well on the way, it's another good round for Heather.

8 — Divorces — 4

A low-scoring round once again, as Mrs and Mr Mills remained happily married until death did them part. In their 4 decades together, their marriage went through only 1 rocky patch. The couple took a holiday in Canada to 'work things out', during which Mrs Mills was trampled by a moose. But the unfortunate event had the effect of bringing them closer together.

Heather can turn her hand to many things, such as charity campaigning, being a Good Will Ambassador for the United Nations and posing with lipstick round her nipples for German grumble mags. However, one thing she has never tried is prospecting for gold. "Swinging a pick-axe all day, then standing in a freezing cold mountain stream sieving grit for hours on end has never really appealed to me," she told NBC's Regus Phitbin. A low scoring round for Lady Macca.

2 — Gold Digging — 9

As a young girl, Mrs had dreams of striking it rich in the American Gold Rush. She crossed the Atlantic and spent four months panning for gold in the Sierra Madre. However, on her way to the Assay Office she was ambushed by leering Mexican bandits who stole her bag of nuggets and her mule. To make matters worse, on the way back to her shack she was attacked by a cougar. She didn't fancy starting again from scratch and returned to London to learn the piano instead.

Oh dear! An accident several years ago saw the model lose a leg, and whilst she clearly deserves full marks for the fantastic way she copes with her disability and the wonderful example she sets for others in the same situation, unfortunately the wording of this round is unambiguous. Rules are rules, so she nets a dismal 0 out of 10.

0 — Full Complement of Two Legs — 15

Mrs scores 10 out of 10 for her two legs. She also bags an extra 5 points, because she was actually born with THREE legs! Her third limb, a full sized rear-facing leg complete with foot, meant that she could play the piano without a stool. But she was very embarrassed about this anatomical curiosity, and always kept it hidden under a long dress.

Oh, dear! A good showing throughout, but brave Heather trips up at the final hurdle. It's a case of close, but no cigar for the soft-hearted northern lovely.

43 — HOW DID THEY DO? — 44

Mrs is Top of the Millses. No doubt she'd be thumping out a rousing victory chorus on an out-of-tune piano surrounded by drunken Pearly Kings, if she were still alive.

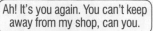

Harry Herring Antiques

Harry Herring's Antique Shop of Mysteries...

Ah! It's you again. You can't keep away from my shop, can you.

You've just caught me having a cup of tea.

Talking of tea, three girls came into my shop 10 years ago to this very day and bought a teapot...

...a bargain... or so they thought!

Hey, look at this. It's just what we need for our flat.

Yeah! It's groovy.

Excuse me. How much for this teapot?

Why, it's £30...

...but I'm afraid you girls could not afford it.

What do you mean? We could all chip in a tenner.

No, no. You misunderstand me...

...you see, this teapot belonged to Ghengis Khan, evil Emperor of the Mongol Empire.

On his deathbed, he vowed that anyone who drank from this teapot would mysteriously lose money.

Ha! What a load of claptrap.

Yes. Your fairy stories don't scare us. We'll take it.

Come on, girls, £10 each.

Very well. But don't say I didn't warn you.

Right! Let's get back to the flat and have a nice cuppa.

Oh, girls! Wait...

Yes? What is it?

I'm so sorry, I forgot. I've got a sale on at the moment. That teapot is not £30...

...it's only £25

Oh! Great!

Here's your change... 5 one pound coins.

Look, why don't we take £1 back each, and give you the other £2 for being so honest.

Thank you, my dear. That's most kind.

Back at the flat...

So much for Genghis Khan's curse about losing money, eh girls.

Yes. We all got a pound of our tenners back. If anything it's a lucky teapot.

Hold on... we all paid £10 and we each got a £1 coin back. That means we paid £9 each.

Yes, and we gave the shop keeper £2. What about it?

Don't you see...?

...3 times £9 is £27... plus the £2 that the shop keeper got makes...

... £29

...so... where did the other £1 go?

SCREAM!!!

Oh, my God!! The curse...

Yes! ...it's come **true!**

A cursed teapot!?! What a ridiculous notion...

...but that one pound must be somewhere. I don't know where. You don't know where...

Perhaps it is forever lost somewhere within...

Harry Herring's Antique Shop of Mysteries!

THE BEIJING OLYMPICS have come and gone, and once again Team GB has failed to deliver. Our shamefaced team of 312 elite Olympians brought back a paltry 18 golds from China. That's equates to a mere one medal between seventeen athletes, which makes Britain's average result in each event a feeble 18th - that's just a sixth of a bronze each. We went out on the street to see what the great British public had to say about this national embarrassment.

...I FOR one am sick of paying for Paula Radcliffe to go on fancy foreign holidays every four years, only for her to return without any medals. At the very least, she should offer to pay for her own mini-bar bills, room service and any adult movies she's watched in her room.

Loris Idris, architectural model-maker

...THERE'S far too much emphasis placed on competition at the Olympics. How much better it would be if everybody came home with a medal, simply for participating nicely.

Janice Lemur, feng shui blackbelt

...WHAT is the point of sending an athlete half way round the world, only for them to come back empty-handed? Unless we are 100% sure that they're going to win gold, we should simply save our money. I ended the Beijing games having won just as many medals as Paula Radcliffe, and I spent the entire fortnight sitting on the sofa in my pants, dipping Doritos in a jar of Chicken Tonight. The cost to the British taxpayer? Zero, If you don't include two weeks' dole money and my housing benefit.

Sid Colobus, jobseeker

...THE ladies' quad rowers who came second to the Chinese had a ruddy nerve bringing their boat back to shore. If they had had an ounce of decency they would have scuttled their craft and gone down with it, like the captain of the Titanic did, and saved us the cost of their air fare home.

Harry Spider, bingo caller

...14-YEAR-old diver Tom Daley should hang his head in shame. If his story had been a film, he would have brought back a gold medal from Beijing. Not only that, he would have won it with his last dive, narrowly beating a Russian who had been cheating all along. All this whilst disguising the fact that he had a broken arm caused by the Russian pushing him over in the changing room just before the final round. In reality, he came a mediocre seventh, and that's without a broken arm.

Vince Bonobo, sandwich engineer

...IT'S often been said that winning is unimportant, as it's the taking part that counts. What utter claptrap. The government should stamp out this silly idea once and for all by awarding New Year's Honours to medal winners, and nothing at all to the losers.

Olive Proboscis, stripper

...ANYONE who doesn't win a medal is worse than a paedophile in my book. They have been taking Britain for a ride for far too long. If I had my way, I'd fine them a thousand pounds each, chemically castrate them and put them on the Sex Offenders' register.

Lord Chief Justice Frank Howler QC, law lord

...IF OUR athletes had merely taken loads of drugs, like the winners probably did, perhaps they would have come back from Beijing with a more impressive haul.

Ulrika Orangutan, proctologist

...WHEN I heard about Britain's feeble performance in Beijing, I put my foot through the television and sent Bert Kwouk the bill.

Harold Marmoset, pygmy breeder

...THE British Olympic authorities could easily increase our tally by offering British passports to gold medal winners from other countries. I'm sure that Jamaican sprinter Usain Bolt, for example, would jump at the chance to live in Britain. Getting stopped and searched by the police four times a day for being black would be a small price to pay for the glory of running for England.

Geoff Mandrill, unicycle courier

...I WOULD happily have paid the bill for Mr Marmoset's television, only I was born in Manchester and I don't see why I should.

Bert Kwouk, actor

...BRITAIN finished fourth in the medals table, so even if there had been medals for winning medals, we would have been pipped for the bronze.

Samson Gibbon, pouffe upholsterer

...MAKING our BMX cyclists ride toddlers' bikes was asking for trouble. No wonder our golden girl Shanaze Reade fell off hers and missed out on a medal.

Anthony Sasquatch, mud wrestler

...I HAD high hopes that Team GB would do us proud in Beijing, but I feel badly let down by the overall performance of our squad. The only athlete who managed to live up to my expectations was tennis ace Andy Murray, who crashed out in the first round. Well done Andy.

Desdemona Capuchin, genuine filthy bored housewife

...THESE Olympic losers have shamed our nation in front of the whole world, yet they expect to come back here and just live amongst us as if nothing has happened. They should be shaved, and forced to wear stripy boilersuits with big pink 'L's on them until 2012.

D Irving, revisionist historian

mr. LOGIC

HE'S A PAIN IN THE ARSE

Viz Comic
PO Box 656
North Shields
NE30 4XX

letters@viz.co.uk

★★★ STAR LETTER ★★★

SCIENTISTS at CERN claim that a ton of helium has leaked into the accelerator chamber. Well, how can you have a ton of helium? It's lighter than air, so you couldn't weigh it. In fact, the more you put on the scales, the less it would weigh.

Rock Brazilliano, e-mail

David Icke claims that the world's economy is run by lizards masquerading as humans, such as George W Bush and Her Majesty the Queen. Why doesn't he simply break into their houses and have a look at their bedrooms? If they sleep on a big rock instead of a bed and have an enormous red light bulb hanging over them, I think the man has a case.

S Alfonso, e-mail

Holly Willoughby does a wonderful job presenting *X Factor Extra* on ITV2. She seems like a very charming young lady, and what's more she scrubs up nicely too. I'd say her husband is a lucky chap (If she has one)!

Gladys, Swansea

I read in the news the other day that police had raided a cocaine factory and found a 'significant amount of cocaine.' What else did they expect to find in a cocaine factory? And how foolish of the manufacturers to open a cocaine factory in the first place. It's just asking for trouble if you ask me.

Edna Battering-Ram, Longfields

I recently visited a chip shop in Hackney and was surprised to find that the food was more expensive if you elected to 'eat in'. It seemed odd to be asked to pay a premium to consume some greasy chips at a dirty table surrounded by questionable characters in the arse end of London. Surely a reduction in price should be in order.

Frampton Lovestrings, London

The Church of England has officially apologised to Charles Darwin and accepted his theory of evolution. But the bible says that God created mankind in his own image, so the church now believe that God is a monkey. Well I for one will not be going to church again.

Edward Teach, e-mail

With reference to the above letter. I too will not be going to church again. I don't know about anyone else, but I refuse to worship a big hairy being that sits around all day on a tyre wanking, drinking from the spout of a teapot and throwing His turds at passing angels.

Grace O'Malley, e-mail

If, as the Church of England says, God was a monkey, that means that the Virgin Mary got her cherry popped off a chimpanzee. Now I've seen that happen on a video that my mate Morris bought into work, and it was not what you would call religiously inspiring spectacle, let me tell you.

Henry Avery, e-mail

With reference to the previous letter. I am a zoologist and I can tell your readers that chimps have surprisingly small penises, just a couple of inches long. Any supreme being worth His salt would be packing something more awe inspiring like that, along the lines of 'Big' John Holmes or King Dong. Honestly, any man I know who could create the universe in a week would have given himself at least a foot of throbbing gristle.

Jack Rackman, e-mail

Is anybody else sick and tired of all these new fangled crisp flavours that seem to be springing up all over the place? Who in their right mind would want to eat crisps which purport to taste of Thai Sweet Chilli or Apple and Herb? I for one shall be sticking to the big three - cheese 'n' onion, ready salted and salt 'n' vinegar - thank you very much!

Kenneth, Guildford

I really like Jaffa Cakes. Sometimes I'll eat three or four in one afternoon!

Darren, Leeds

I read with interest Craig Eddie's letter *(last issue)* concerning the Barbary ape in Gibraltar which felt his wife's tit and ran away. Me and my mates were posted in Gibraltar on a short tour in the army and we spent a weekend on the Rock with a bottle of Smirnoff and 200 fags. We decided to teach the monkeys to drink and smoke, and the episode Mr Eddie describes may be as a result of us squaddies teaching the monkeys all we know. I'd like to say that me and my army pals are extremely proud of our accomplishments and hope that we can get back to Gibraltar to finish the monkeys' training.

Dinger, The Army

When Richard Hammond was fighting for his life after his high-speed crash I, like the majority of the population, was wishing him a full and speedy recovery. Now, however, after seeing those Morrisons adverts on the telly, I can't help wondering if we weren't all a little hasty.

Derek Derekson, e-mail

My 94-year-old nana is always reminding people that she is a great, great, great grandmother. I for one would have expected a little more modesty from a woman of her generation.

Darren Conway, e-mail

Usain Bolt's two gold medals in the Olympics are all well and good, but running quickly in a straight line isn't going to put food on the table, is it? I think he'd do well to settle down and learn a trade while he's a young man. My grandson is a dentist and he's got a five door Ford Focus.

Qango Tackhammer, e-mail

I don't understand these people who say they have a fear of flying. When you're on a plane at 35,000 feet, flying is the optimum scenario.

Martin Christmas, Leeds

People are always going on about how drink-drivers kill hundreds of people a year. What they forget is that we all have to die of something.

H Turpentine, e-mail

George Michael VOX POP

IT SEEMS that we can't open a newspaper without reading lurid accounts of pop superstar GEORGE MICHAEL's seedy antics. If he's not in a public lavatory taking a heady cocktail of drugs, he's out on Hampstead Heath bumming a van driver in a bush. It's a far cry from the fresh-faced hunk who won the nation's hearts back in the 80s. His stomach-turning carryings on have got the whole nation talking, so we went out on the streets to gauge the public mood and find out what THREE of you thought...

...THERE may be a perfectly innocent explanation for Michael's previous misadventures. For all we know, the van driver may have been choking in a bush and Michael was performing the Heimlich manoeuvre to clear the obstacle, during the course of which both of their trousers may have fallen down. Far from pillorying George, we should be giving him a medal for saving this man's life.

Benjamin Horngold, road sweeper

...I HAVE no sympathy with this man who needs to be cured of his sickness. I would do this by showing him photographs of naked van drivers in bushes whilst giving him mild electric shocks to the genitals and increasing the voltage if he becomes aroused.

Bartholomew Roberts, lollipop man

...IF GEORGE has a fascination with sex in public toilets, why doesn't he build a toilet block in the grounds of his house and employ actors to come in and bum him?

Anne Bonney, lollipop lady

Nelson's Column

IT'S THE RUMOUR MONGER WITH THE BEST VIEW IN LONDON!

...so let's see what exciting things Admiral Lord Nelson has spied from his panoramic vantage point this week:

Ahoy there! So, in the early hours of Monday morning I saw TV presenters **Fearne Cotton** and **Holly Willoughby** waiting for a night bus. They were singing drunkenly and shouting abuse at passing cars. Shocking eh? I think it was them anyway. It was definitely two blonde women. I'm quite high up so I can't make out much detail unfortunately.

★ ★ ★ ★ ★ ★ ★ ★ ★ ★ ★ ★ ★

All hands on deck! So, on Thursday afternoon I saw **Wayne Rooney** and his wife **Colleen**. They were getting out of a car and going into a restaurant. It looked like they were having a pretty heated discussion. Well, well, well, I thought to myself, here's some juicy gossip! But unfortunately I couldn't hear what they were saying, on account of the fact that I'm quite high up.

★ ★ ★ ★ ★ ★ ★ ★ ★ ★ ★ ★ ★

Man overboard! So, on Friday night there was a film premiere in nearby Leicester Square. All those celebrities in one place, I thought to myself. Names like **Jack Black, Robert Downey Jr, Uma Thurman** and **Ben Afleck**... just imagine the amount of gossip I'll get hold of! Unfortunately I had forgotten that I'm posed in a rigid position with my gaze fixed in the direction of Big Ben, so I couldn't actually see any of the action going on behind me. Or hear it. Sorry!

More titbits next week. And remember, from 169 feet above London, no celeb is safe from my watchful eye!

TOP TIPS TOP TIPS TOP TIPS TOP TIPS

OLD people. Each night, go to sleep in the recovery position, potentially saving paramedics valuable time.

Kev Pick, e-mail

FITNESS fanatics. When driving to the gym, spend half an hour circling the car park so as to nab a spot as close as possible to the door. That way you won't waste any energy before you embark on your two-hour workout.

Vic C, Bedford

SAVE money on expensive air fresheners by sticking lavender un your arse. Then everytime you fart, a burst of soothing fragrance is released into your home..

M Hinge, e-mail

GENTLEMEN. Upon leaving your favourite adult store into a busy street, affect an expression of utter shock, just in case.

John Mitchell, e-mail

HOMELESS people. Take the piss by asking for money 'for a cup of tea' whilst pissed out of your face on Special Brew.

Graham Purple, e-mail

Super jumper!

I knitted it myself!

Men! Keep warm this winter with a fantastic Viz jumper you can knit yourself.

Your step by step guide:

Materials (for jumper or tank top): Balls of wool in two colours, knitting needles.

Instructions (for medium sized jumper): Take the end of the wool and cast on by looping it over one of the needles. Put the other needle in it and move them up and down so it makes a clicky clacky noise. Occasionally stop to pull some more wool off the ball. Change to the different wool to knit the logo. Continue knitting until it is jumper shaped. For bigger fittings, continue knitting for slightly longer. Then do the sleeves in the same way, remembering to knit them the same length as your arms. For the tank top version, simply cut the sleeves off with scissors after you have knitted them. Cast off by removing the knitting needles from the jumper.

Lovely Jumper or smashing Tank Top. The choice is YOURS!

Have Your Say...

ACTRESS SUE JONES-DAVIS was probably best known for her role as Judith in Monty Python's *The Life of Brian*. In one scene she famously appeared full frontal nude, but like many actors, was happy to do so as it was essential to the plot. But could that decision come back to haunt her, for Jones-Davis is now the Lord Mayor of Aberystwyth? Does it matter that we have all seen her pubes? Does it demonstrate that despite being a Lord Mayor, she is just an ordinary person like one of her subjects, or does the fact that we know she's got a right old biffer on her lessen the dignity of her office? We went on the streets to find out what YOU think...

Jones-Davis as the Lord Mayor of Aberystwyth yesterday and as Life of Brian's Judith (inset)

...IT ill befits any Lord Mayor to have their pubic hair on display to all and sundry. I think that on being elected to any public office, people should have their pubic hairs shaved off so that this sort of thing can never happen.

H Brandenburg, Herts

...IT'S not the first time that someone in public office has had their pubes on display to the general public. Glenda Jackson MP got them out in the film The Music Lovers, and more recently Welsh Minister Ron Davies gave his an airing whilst looking for badgers in a layby somewhere.

Tarquin Milk, Runcorn

...I THINK it's an absolute disgrace that Jones-Davies should take up public office. Thirty years ago she was showing all she's got to anybody who wanted to see it, and today she's judging sand castle competitions for children!

M Tonbridge, Luton

...IT'S an appalling situation where somebody can reveal their pubic hair for profit, and then be put in charge of the civic finances of one of the finest cities in Wales. What is this country coming to?

T Bootle, Wigan

...I THINK it's marvellous that I have seen my Lord Mayor's bush. How many other people outside of Aberystwyth can say the same? Good on ya, Sue.

T Pinner, Aberystwith

...I BEG to differ with T Pinner (above letter). I live in London and I have seen Lord Mayor Boris Johnson's unruly pubes. Mind you, I'm married to him so that probably doesn't count.

Mrs B Johnson, London

...I THINK anyone who reveals their intimate bodily hair to anyone other than their spouse or their doctor should be banned from holding any public office whatsoever and put on the sex offenders register.

H Monkton, Croydon

...I LIVE in Aberystwyth and recently received a legal notice from the council telling me I had to cut my hedge which is blocking a pavement. The hypocrisy is staggering since, if her appearance in The Life of Brian is anything to go by, Jones-Davies is unwilling to trim her own thick foliage.

M Fibreboard, Aberystwyth

...I WAS so appalled when I heard on the news that Jones-Davies had become Lord mayor of Aberystwyth, that I put my foot through the telly and sent her the bill. Then my wife pointed out that we were actually listening to the news on the radio, not the TV. So I put my foot through the radio and sent her the bill for that, too.

J Braithwaite, Mull

...JONES-DAVIES has demonstrated that she is not averse to displaying her pubery in public. I think the possibility of her giving everyone a little flash of her wotnot will add a little frisson of excitement to otherwise boring civic meetings and plaque unveiling ceremonies.

M Broughton, Solihul

...I WAS elected to my local council in 1970 and have never see any of the serving Lord Mayors' pubes. By electing Jones-Davies, the councillors of Aberystwyth have achieved in one stroke what I have never achieved in nearly forty years of office.

Councillor L Plywood, Otley

I'M ON AN EARLY SHIFT TOMORROW, SO I'M SETTING MY TEASMAID TO WAKE ME UP AT 6AM...WITH A LOVELY CUP OF TEA...!

RIGHT THEN...ONE FINAL CHECK BEFORE LIGHTS OUT. CUP...SAUCER...SPOON...MILK... TWO SUGARS...I'VE FILLED THE POT WITH WATER...

...AND JUST IN CASE THERE'S A POWER-CUT DURING THE NIGHT...

...I'VE GOT IT PLUGGED INTO A DIESEL GENERATOR AT THE END OF THE BED!

6.00 NEXT MORNING... BEEP! BEEP! BEEP!

SQUIRT! GURGLE! BUBBLE! MASH! YAWN! FLAP-FLAP TEA'S UP!

ACE! I CAN'T WAIT FOR ME FIRST SIP..! SIP!

SLOOP!

SPLOOT! GAK!..KA!KA!KA! COUGH!...EEE-EEEW! I FORGOT TO PUT THE FUCKING BAG IN. GAAH!

SHORTLY... RIGHT! -TIME FOR MY FIRST TEA-BREAK OF THE DAY, I THINK. POLICE STATION TAILORED LAW ENFORCEMENT SOLUTIONS WATCH THIS!

ALRIGHT SUNSHINE...GIZ A CUPPA AND I'LL "FORGET" ABOUT NICKING YOU FOR OBSTRUCTION OF HER MAJESTY'S PAVEMENT... CAPEESH? BOB'S TEA WAGON TEA 10P HERE YOU GO, KETTLE. MILK AND 2 SUGARS AS USUAL.

BLOW-BLOW...OOH, THIS IS GOING TO BE THE BEST DRINK OF THE DAY - I CAN ALMOST TASTE IT ALREADY..!

WHAT THE..?! GRAB! THANKS OFFICER. THIS CUP OF HOT, SWEET TEA IS JUST WHAT I NEED! THAT MAN HAS JUST BEEN HIT BY A CAR AND IT WILL STOP HIM GOING INTO SHOCK... ...PROBABLY. ST JOHN'S AMBULANCE

HMM...THAT GIVES ME AN IDEA.

HEH-HEH! WHEN THAT EXPERIMENTAL ULTRA-LIGHTWEIGHT MILK-FLOAT DRIVES OVER MY FOOT, IT'LL BE FREE TEA ALL THE WAY!

HERE WE GO..! GRATIS CHAR HERE I...

...COME... SWERVE! HUNH!?

RUMBLE RUMBLE!? EXPERIMENTAL ULTRA HEAVYWEIGHT STEAMROLLER RUMBLE!

SPLAT!

SHORTLY... INTENSIVE CARE UNIT NIL TEA BY MOUTH RATS' COCKS.

NOT ICE TO SEE YOU, TO SEE YOU, NOT ICE!

Pole dancer: Forsythe is ecological time bomb, says boffin.

A GLOBAL WARMING expert has urged veteran entertainer Bruce Forsyth to stay away from the North Pole, fearing the tap-dancing octogenarian could start a chain of events which could end life on Earth as we know it.

According to London-based academic Ed Barge, the ice sheets of the polar region are now so thin that just 'a single tap' from one of Brucie's trademark shoes could send millions of tons of ice sliding into the sea. The resulting tsunami would crash into the shores of Europe and North America, killing millions and making many more homeless.

nightmare

Barge, 53, told reporters that he came up with the nightmarish scenario after a heavy drinking session. "I was lying face down on my laboratory floor one Saturday night. As I drifted in and out of consciousness I could hear Brucie hosting Strictly Come Dancing on the TV in the kitchen. Later on I came to again to hear David Attenborough talking about the dangers

EXCLUSIVE!

of the melting ice caps. The sheer horror of the two worlds colliding hit me like a hammer."

The next day Barge caught the bus to Brucie's home town of Wentworth in a bid to prevent this nightmare scenario becoming reality. "I decided that I had to get to the Gen Game host before he inadvertently killed us all," he said. "I managed to climb over the fence his £10m mansion and was just entering his bedroom when the police arrived. I explained that I was trying to prevent an ecological tragedy but they took me back to the police station where they beat me up a bit."

Despite being given a caution, Barge vowed to continue his crusade to stop Mr Forsyth ever setting foot on the polar ice shelf. "I couldn't let the prospect of a police record stop me from trying to save the planet," he told reporters. "I waited until I knew he was in and scaled the fence again. Once inside, I tied both him and his former Miss World wife up and bundled them into the cellar. However the police arrived again and this time I was given a proper kicking. I'm in court at the end of the month. My only hope is that Brucie reads this and realises how much danger he's putting us all in."

nightnurse

When we contacted the performer's agent for a comment we were told that Forsyth had no intention of tap-dancing at the north pole. Or anywhere else outside a regulation ballroom dance floor. "Bruce is very aware of his responsibilities to the environment and would never take any action that could cause millions of tons of ice to slide into the sea," he told us.

Yesterday, Barge pleaded guilty to twenty charges of breaking and entering, aggravated burglary and going equipped. He was remanded in custody pending psychiatric reports.

UP THE RSC

CORNER

Sender: J. Frost, Bedford (plus loads of others)

Bishop of York's Para Drop was Kids' Stuff ~

ARCHBISHOP OF DANGER

IN A DAREDEVIL STUNT, Archbishop of York Dr John Sentamu recently hit the headlines around the world when he made a Red Devil-style parachute jump. The publicity-hungry cleric leapt from 12,500 feet, free-falling for 45 seconds before opening his chute and performing a textbook landing at RAF Langar in Nottinghamshire. In the process, the 59-year-old priest won widespread respect and raised over £50,000 for military charities.

But Sentamu's action-packed airborne escapade didn't go down well with everyone. In an outspoken sermon, Archbishop of Canturbury Dr Rowan Williams later branded the stunt 'kids' stuff'. "It really was quite a tame thing to do when you compare it to some of the extreme stuff I've got up to," he told a packed Westminster Abbey last Sunday. "It may have looked exciting to the uninitiated, but to someone who lives life at the pace that I do, a tandem parachute jump really is run of the mill stuff."

LID

And now in a new book, *Archbishop of Danger - Under the Cassock*, Williams lifts the lid on his secret, thrill-seeking life. Here, in a series of exclusive extracts, we reveal the death-defying exploits that will astound a public who know him only as a mild-mannered man of God...

MARKS

With his mitre, crook and ceremonial vestments, the Archbishop of Canterbury is a familiar sight at ceremonial events, state funerals

VALLEY OF THE SHADOW OF DEATH: Williams planned suicidal jet-bike leap.

and remembrance services. But few people would expect to see him in a set of garish motorcycle leathers and a cape, sitting astride a rocket-powered motorbike at the base of a 500-foot ramp.

"A couple of years ago, I had this fantastic idea of jumping over the Grand Canyon on a rocket-powered bike. It was a suicidal stunt, I knew that if anything went wrong, I faced a two mile drop to certain doom. Even if it went right I still had to face a 250mph landing on the opposite, rubble-strewn bank. So I prayed to God to ask if it was it was a good idea. He told me that I must be completely crazy, but I just laughed, because that's the kind of bishop I am.

SPENCER

The next day, I found myself on the edge of the Grand Canyon astride 2000 horse powers of jet-bike. Sitting on the launchpad, I ran through a mental checklist of 'what ifs'. What if the engine exploded? What if a gust of wind blew me away from the landing strip and smashed me into the canyon face at the speed of sound? What if the tyres disintegrated under the 20 G-force acceleration up the nearly vertical ramp? I was nervous, I'll admit. But then I remembered the Eleventh Commandment, one I had written myself... Thou Shalt Not Chicken Out!

The countdown had begun. With five seconds

> ## "The sense of latent power between my legs was intoxicating"

to go I revved my engines to maximum thrust and got ready to dial in the afterburner.

LANCE

The sense of latent power between my legs was intoxicating as the bike strained against the brakes like a wild stallion. All thoughts of danger left my mind and my only thought was of piloting that bike across the canyon and into the record books. Everything was in slow motion now, and despite the deafening banshee scream of the engines all I could hear was the steady beat of my heart.

It was now or never. My thumb was hovering over the launch button on the handlebars, but then I suddenly remembered that I had promised to judge a home-made jam competition that afternoon for the Canterbury Women's Institute. Reluctantly I aborted the jump. Had I made that leap, it would have been the greatest stunt ever pulled by a bishop.

Later that day, I awarded first prize in the jam competition to a jar of particularly-nice seedless fruits of the forest preserve. I couldn't help thinking that if the women in the audience had seen me just hours before, sitting in my leathers astride my rocket-powered jet-bike on the brink of a canyon of death, then they wouldn't keep going on about how great the Archbishop of York is."

WATERFALL STUNT WAS LEAP OF FAITH

You might expect your local bishop to occasionally go over the Ten Commandments in his pulpit, but chances

FALL FROM GRACE: Bishop planned barrel drop.

are you'd be amazed to discover that he was planning to go over the world's highest waterfall... in a barrel. But that's just what Dr Williams decided to do to celebrate his appointment as Archbishop of Wales.

PIKE

"When you think about going over waterfalls in a barrel, you automatically think of Niagara Falls. But Niagara is only about 170 feet high - the sort of drop that a soft, show-off bishop like Dr John Sentamu might do. I set my sights a bit higher - over TWENTY TIMES higher, in fact! And that's how I found myself sitting in a beer barrel, bobbing about in the foaming rapids at the top of the Angel Falls in Venezuela. The water was so rough that I had to fasten my bishop's hat on with an elastic band.

This truly was a leap of faith of every sense of the word. Nobody had ever made it down those falls alive, and even if I did survive the drop there was every chance I'd get bitten to death by the man-eating piranhas which gather in the whirlpool which swirls at their base. As my barrel drifted inexorably towards the overhang, my speed increasing with every second as the powerful current dragged me to my inevitable fate, the adrenalin rush was incredible. My barrel was now just inches from the edge. The thundering roar of mil-

Shocking Verdict from

DARE ANGEL: Archbishop of Canterbury Dr Rowan Williams with his carefully-teased owl-like eyebrows yesterday.

CRATER LOVE HATH NO MAN: Williams fancied chances in volcano shot.

---

lions of gallons of raging water filled my senses, I felt the boiling spray stinging my bishop's cheeks. *I was just seconds away from almost certain death, yet I had never felt so alive.*

WILSON

Then, as my barrel teetered on the brink and I was looking down into the 3,000 foot foaming maelstrom beneath me, it suddenly occurred to me that I hadn't written the introduction to my weekly parish newsletter yet. I knew that it was going to the printers that afternoon, so I had no choice but to turn back. Disconsolately, I paddled my way to the bank and clambered out of my barrel and onto the grass. It was such a disappointment. Had I been able to carry my plan through, it would certainly been the bravest thing attempted by a suffragan bishop of the Anglican Communion ever. It would definitely have put certain other so-called 'stunts', carried out by certain other bishops who shall remain nameless, well and truly in the shade, I can tell you."

FIRE & BRIMSTONE HELD NO FEAR FOR BISHOP

Everyone's heard the old religious joke "Tell the Canon he's fired." But, when Dr Williams was appointed Canon of Christchurch College, Oxford, it was very quip that gave him the idea for his most audacious stunt yet.

MACMILLAN

"The prospect of being shot from a giant gun had always appealed to my daredevil side. The only problem was, whilst it might have been dangerous enough for a lesser, headline-hungry bishop, it was simply too tame and wussy for me! So when I heard that Mauna Loa, the world's most dangerous volcano, had erupted and was belching white hot lather, spume and molten rock high into the Hawaii sky, I immediately packed my toothbrush, crash helmet and giant cannon.

HEATH

My plan was to douse myself with petrol before being blasted right over the erupting volcano. The intense heat from the white hot magma over which I was flying would ignite the petrol, turning me into a spectacular human fireball. If everything went according to plan, I was to land in a child's paddling pool on the other side of the crater. This would hopefully cushion my landing and extinguish the flames. However, I knew I was taking a huge risk. If my trajectory was anything other than inch perfect, I would be dashed to death on the spiky pumice and then burnt to a crisp before help could arrive.

Everybody told me it couldn't be done, but then I remembered our Lord Jesus Christ. When they told him it was impossible to walk on water, he didn't bottle out. He stepped up to the plate and proved them wrong. Now it was my turn!

And so I found myself soaked in petrol, sitting on top of half a ton of TNT at the bottom of a 200-foot super-gun barrel. Ahead of me, all I could see was a small, blue circle of sky. In those few, final seconds before giving the order to fire, all my senses were heightened. The smell of petrol combined with the sulphurous gases, making a heady, high-octane cocktail of danger and excitement. Every nerve and sinew in my body tingled with the anticipation of what I was about to do. I braced myself against the dynamite

as I heard my choirmaster, Mr Posner, strike the match to light the fuse. I held out my fists in front of me as I readied myself, waiting for the inevitable shockwave from the massive detonation beneath my feet.

It was then that a thought hit me. I had to get back to Wales, where I was expected at my local radio studios to record my popular 2-minute 'Time for a Think' spot, which went out on BBC Radio Monmouth every Sunday between the morning shipping forecast and the farming outlook programme. It was a real sickener, but I had no option but to cancel the firing and get to the airport. As I climbed out of the emergency escape hatch, I wistfully reflected on what my listeners would have thought if they knew that I had almost been fired from a cannon over an erupting volcano, whilst doused with petrol, into a shallow paddling pool of water."

HEAVENLY JUMP WAS HIGH RISK STRATEGY

Bishops are used to wrestling with complex moral quandaries, ecumenical problems and theological conundrums. But few can claim to have wrestled a tiger... 5 miles above the earth!

OFFICE

"I'd given up defying death for lent, but now it was Easter Saturday and my danger fast was at an end. Forty days build up of adrenalin was coursing through my veins; I knew I had to do something to slake my ravenous thirst for risk. I dreamed up my most extreme stunt yet. We took off in a light aircraft and flew to a height of 25,000 feet. In the plane, my verger strapped me into a straitjacket before taking my parachute and fastening it onto a hungry tiger. After this, he got a hunting knife and locked it into a safe. The stunt was to go like this... once we were over the drop-zone, the tiger would be pushed out of the door, followed at 10-second intervals by the safe, and then by me. My task was to somehow escape from the straitjacket, then catch up with the safe. After cracking it and getting the knife, I had to catch up with the tiger, wrestle it and stab it to death. Only then could I remove the parachute from its back, put it on and pull the ripcord. It was a risky plan; if I got a single part of it wrong I'd end up spread across the landing site like so much strawberry jam.

The door opened and the cold rush of wind hit the cabin. The green drop light went on and my verger pushed the snarling tiger out of the plane. I watched as the doomed beast hurtled towards the ground, quickly becoming a tiny dark speck as it thrashed its razor-sharp claws wildly. Ten seconds later, the safe followed it out of the door. As it tumbled away from the plane, I knew that locked within its six-inch thick steel shell was my only hope of getting out of this alive. The verger turned to me, on his face was etched a rictus of concern. "You know, Dr Williams," he shouted across the boom of the engines and the roar of the wind. "It's not too late to back out."

RELATIONS

But standing there in the doorway of that plane, strapped in a straitjacket five miles in the air, with my parachute on a tiger thousands of feet below me, I knew there was no turning back. I had to go through with this. I was just about to jump when the pilot received a message from my secretary at Westminster Abbey, Mrs Simmonds. Apparently, the gift shop had run out of souvenir pencil sharpeners and I'd accidentally come out with the key to the stock cupboard in my pocket.

GRACIE

Reluctantly, I had no choice but to call off the stunt at the eleventh hour. As the plane landed and I stepped out onto the airfield, I really regretted missing yet another opportunity to cock a snook at the grim reaper. Archbishop Hey-everybody-look-at-me Sentamu may think he's made of the right stuff, but until he has stabbed a tiger whilst hurtling towards certain death at 150mph, he can keep his big mouth shut."

NEXT WEEK: *How I was about to do a 20-mile bungee-jump from the edge of space into a shark-infested swimming pool filled with cyanide and poisonous snakes, until I remembered I had left the font running.*

Extracts from *Archbishop of Danger - Under the Cassock* by Dr Rowan Williams (Poached Egg Books, £8.99).

> ## "I was just seconds away from almost certain death, yet I had never felt so alive"

Goodbye cruel world... love **SUICIDAL SYD** x

WOW! IT'S SNOWING IN APRIL! MOTHER NATURE NEVER FAILS TO DELIGHT AND SURPRISE US.

LIGHT FLURRY

THEN AGAIN, THIS IS A CLEAR SIGN OF GLOBAL WARMING! WHAT'S NEXT? HURRICANES IN JULY? FLOODS AGAIN? MORE EARTHQUAKES, WITH EACH ONE MORE DEVASTATING THAN THE LAST?

I'M NOT HANGING ABOUT TO STRUGGLE FOR SURVIVAL IN SOME POST-APOCALYPTIC WASTELAND RULED BY APES OR WHATEVER. I'M SO DEPRESSED BY SUCH GRIM PROSPECTS THAT I'M GOING TO KILL MYSELF RIGHT NOW!

GLOOM

HO-HO! I'M RECKLESSLY IGNORING THE ADVICE OF FOOD SAFETY WATCHDOGS AND I'M GOING TO EAT THIS MASSIVE BAG OF ARTIFICIALLY COLOURED SWEETS IN ONE SITTING!

CRAPPY SHOPPER
SWEETS

THE RED ONES ALONE SHOULD SEND ME INTO SUCH A HYPERACTIVE FRENZY I'LL PROBABLY RUN STRAIGHT UNDER A LORRY OR SOMETHING.

BOLLOCKS! I CAN'T EVEN OPEN THE PACKAGING THANKS TO STRINGENT NEW E.U. RULES MAKING SUCH BAGS TAMPER-PROOF!

NO VISIT TO THE PEARLY GATES FOR ME USING THIS METHOD THEN!

SWEETS

LATER... THIS IDEA IS BOUND TO KILL ME OFF. I'M DISGUISED AS A POLISH PLUMBER TOUTING FOR TRADE AROUND THIS RUN DOWN COUNCIL ESTATE. THE LOCAL JOB-SEEKERS WILL STRING ME UP IN NO TIME.

SLAVIC SZYD'S PLUMBING COMPANY FIX YOUR SINK CHEAP

BAH! THERE'S A SPECIAL OFFER ON LAGER AT THE OFF-LICENSE AND THEY'RE TOO PISSED TO DO ANY LYNCHING TODAY.

FAGS + BOOZE
SLAVIC SZYD'S PLUMBING FIX YOUR SINK CHEAP
WHU THE FU-FU-FU--ZZZZ

:TCHAA!: AND I WAS SO LOOKING FORWARD TO MEETING MY MAKER.

LATER STILL... PERHAPS I'M BEING TOO QUIRKY IN MY SUICIDAL HI-JINX. I THINK I'LL TRY THE TRIED AND TRUE METHOD OF JUMPING OFF THE TOP OF THE HIGHEST BUILDING IN TOWN!

SORRY SYD BUT DUE TO THE CREDIT CRUNCH CAUSED BY THE COLLAPSE IN THE U.S. SUB-PRIME MORTGAGE SECTOR THERE'S A QUEUE OF JUMPERS ON THIS ROOF. YOU'LL HAVE TO TAKE A TICKET AND WAIT YOUR TURN.

NOW JUMPING TICKET Nº 006
527
RAT'S NADS! IT'LL TAKE HOURS!

GAH! IT'S RAINING NOW TOO. I'M NOT WAITING AROUND TO CATCH MY DEATH OF COLD. I'M OFF!

HMM... THE DEATH-BY-PLUMMETING-OFF-A-ROOF SCENARIO STILL APPEALS TO ME THOUGH. PERHAPS I CAN COME UP WITH A SPIN ON THE SAME THEME.

:CHORTLE!: I KNOW! I'LL REPLACE MY TV ARIEL WHILST WEARING AN EMU PUPPET ON ONE ARM. A SURE FIRE RECIPE FOR DISASTER!

IN THIS WET WEATHER I'M BOUND TO LOSE MY FOOTING AND PLUNGE TO MY DOOM.

HERE I GO READERS! SEE YOU IN THE AFTERLIFE.

SLIP!

DOG'S COCKS! I'D FORGOTTEN MY SCUMBAG NEIGHBOUR HAD A PILE OF DISCARDED OLD MATTRESSES IN HER GARDEN.

FLUMP!

FANTASTIC STUFF SYD! I'M HARRY HILL, FROM OFF THE TELLY, AND I'VE JUST FILMED YOUR COMEDY FALL ON MY MOBILE PHONE.

UH?

WE CAN USE THIS CLIP ON *YOU'VE BEEN FRAMED*. HERE'S £250.

WOW! CHEERS!

NEXT DAY... GUESS WHAT CHUMS? THAT CLIP TURNED ME INTO AN OVERNIGHT TV CELEBRITY!

Restaurant de Posh
Theatre

I'VE BEEN INTERVIEWED BY ALL THE TABLOIDS AND I'M SET TO BECOME A REGULAR RENTAGOB ON CHANNEL 4 CLIP SHOWS.

MY LIFE HAS BEEN TURNED AROUND 180°, I'VE BEEN ON A JOURNEY, AND SUBSEQUENTLY I NO LONGER FEEL LIKE KILLING MYSELF. HOORAY!

SMILE!

BLAM!

NEWSAGENT
MY HERO
NEWS
CELEBRITY STALKER ESCAPES FROM MENTAL HOME

LEW STRINGER VIZ 176

142

DANNY'S INFERNO

YOUNG DANNY ALIGHIERI WAS THE LUCKY OWNER OF HIS VERY OWN PORTABLE HELL IN A HANDCART

THE LORD MAYOR IS OPENING A NEW MUNICIPAL RUBBISH BIN IN THE PARK TODAY

SO I'M OFF TO WATCH THE CEREMONY WITH MY INFERNAL PIT OF EVERLASTING TORMENT, ON WHEELS.

BUT OH DEAR! CONSTRUCTION OF THE BIN HASN'T BEEN COMPLETED IN TIME — NOW MY HUSBAND'S GOT NOTHING TO OPEN

G-GOT TO CUT A RIBBON.. OR JUDGE A SANDCASTLE.. ANYTHING!

HE'S SUFFERING ACUTE WITHDRAWAL FROM MAYORAL DUTIES.

GASP! I'M SURE THOSE OMINOUS WROUGHT-IRON GATES WOULD BENEFIT FROM AN OFFICIAL OPENING CEREMONY!!

OO-ER! I WOULDN'T OPEN THEM GATES, MR MAYOR

IT GIVES ME GREAT PLEASURE TO-AWK! ROAR

YOINKS! THE MAYOR HAS BEEN CAST INTO THE FIRES OF PERPETUAL ANGUISH.

SORRY, MISSUS. I'M AFRAID YOUR HUSBAND IS CONDEMNED TO SPEND ALL OF ETERNITY HAVING HIS ASTROLOGICAL STAR CHART EXPLAINED TO HIM WHILST EATING SCOTCH EGG CRUMBS OUT OF STEPHEN GREEN'S BEARD, INSIDE THE BUM-CRACK OF AN ENORMOUS JEREMY CLARKSON.

Christian Voice — TIME TO REPENT!

MUNCH!

BAH! YOU AND YOUR PESKY PORTABLE UNDERWORLD!

WHAT AM I SUPPOSED TO DO WHILE MY HUSBAND WRITHES CEASELESSLY IN THE ABYSS?

PARDON ME MA'AM, I COULDN'T HELP OVERHEARING WHAT YOU SAID

I AM THE EDITOR OF THE WEEKLY WOMEN'S MAGAZINE, CHIT-CHAT..

SHORTLY

THAT MAGAZINE PAID ME FIFTY POUNDS FOR THE TRUE-LIFE STORY OF MY HUSBAND'S SUFFERING

IF I WHORE THE STORY ROUND ALL THE OTHER MAGAZINES TOO, I'LL EARN A PRETTY PENNY!

THANKS DANNY! HERE'S A BAG OF SWEETS FOR YOU — AND A SACK OF CHARCOAL BRIQUETTES FOR YOUR SUPER REALM OF ABADDON, KINGDOM OF DOOM!

HOORAY!

BISCUITS Alive!

THE QUEEN'S OPENING THE NEW MUNICIPAL SEWAGE WORKS TODAY, SO I'M GOING ALONG TO WATCH..!

OOPS! I JUST REMEMBERED... I DON'T KNOW THE WAY!

WE DO!

WHO SAID THAT?

WE DID!

CRUMBS..! MY BISCUITS HAVE COME ALIVE!

FOLLOW US! THE CEREMONY IS OVER HERE!

ACE!

GOSH! I'M JUST IN TIME..!

GRAND ROYAL OPENING TODAY!

..SHE'S ABOUT TO START!

I HEREBY DECLARE THIS SHIT FARM WELL AND TRULY OPEN.

HIP-HIP HOORAY!

BRAVO YOUR MAJESTY!

SQUEAK SQUEAK

RIGHT. THAT'S ME DONE. I'M OFF.

MAIN TURD VALVE

VROOM!

GOD SAVE THE QUEEN!

..AND GOD SAVE MY BISCUITS!

MORE FUN WITH BISCUITS ALIVE IN ANOTHER 18 YEARS.

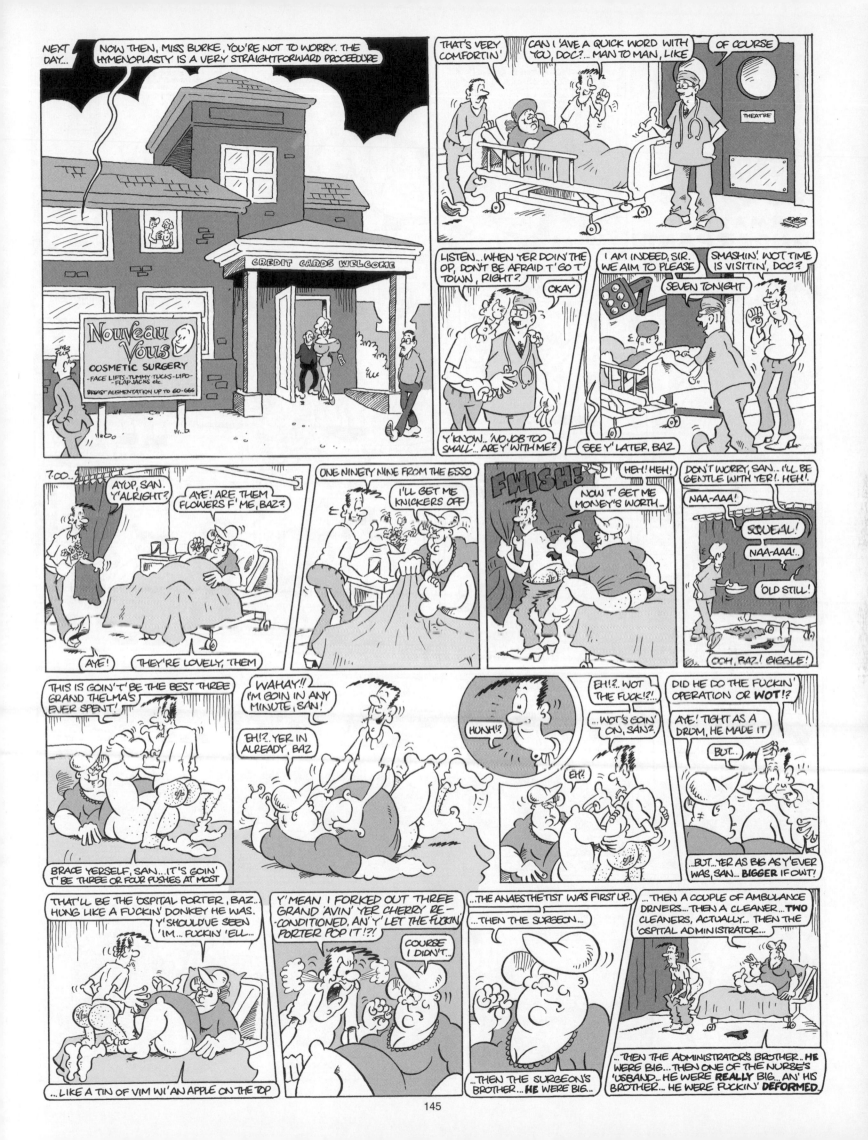

FELIX and his AMAZING UNDERPANTS

FELIX! WHAT'S ALL THIS ABOUT YOU GASSING FARMER BROWN'S NEW BORN CHICKS?

OO-ER!

IT WAS AN ACCIDENT, DAD! YOU SEE THE CHICKS LOOKED COLD, SO I POPPED THEM INTO MY AMAZING UNDERPANTS TO WARM THEM UP. THEN, WITHOUT WARNING, MY BOTTOM...

SPARE ME THE DETAILS!

SUFFICE TO SAY, I'VE BEEN LANDED WITH THE BILL.

HONESTLY, FELIX! I'VE GOT ENOUGH FINANCIAL WORRIES WITHOUT YOUR UNDERPANT ANTICS ADDING TO MY WOES.

THE BARNTON AND FULCHESTER BUILDING SOCIETY IS TEETERING ON THE BRINK OF COLLAPSE — AND I'VE GOT ALL MY LIFE SAVINGS IN THERE!

I'D BETTER TAKE MY SAVINGS OUT, OR I COULD LOSE THE LOT. BUT WHERE TO PUT THEM INSTEAD? ALL THE BANKING INSTITUTIONS SEEM A BIT INSECURE AT PRESENT —

I'VE AN IDEA, DAD..

AND SHORTLY, OUTSIDE THE BUILDING SOCIETY

FELIX, ARE YOU SURE IT'S A GOOD IDEA TO KEEP ALL MY MONEY IN YOUR SHREDDIES?

ABSOLUTELY, DAD! MY AMAZING UNDERPANTS ARE GUARANTEED 100% SAFE. JUST BUNG IT ALL IN!

EXCUSE ME ~ CAN I KEEP MY MONEY IN YOUR PANTS, TOO?

AND ME

MINE ALSO!

SHORTLY

I'VE HAD SO MANY PEOPLE PUTTING THEIR MONEY INTO MY UNDERCRACKERS, I'VE HAD TO FIT A CASHPOINT MACHINE TO THE FRONT

I'D LIKE TO WITHDRAW TWENTY POUNDS, FELIX

HOY! YOUR MACHINE HAS JUST SWALLOWED UP MY CARD!

SORRY, DUE TO AN INCREASE IN PANT CHARGES, YOU ARE NOW IN EXCESS OF YOUR OVERDRAFT LIMIT.

BUT FEEL FREE TO POP INTO MY UNDERPANTS DURING NORMAL BANKING HOURS TO DISCUSS THIS MATTER

CRUNCH

GNN!

I'LL FEEL FREE TO POP MY KNEE INTO YOUR BOLLOCKS!

BLOODY UNDERPANT BANKS.

NOW IF YOU DON'T MIND, I'LL TAKE THAT TWENTY QUID. THANK YOU.

OOYAH! MY POOR PODS! THAT WAS A REAL CREDIT CRUNCH!

I'VE HIRED A COUPLE OF ARMED GUARDS TO PROTECT MY PANTS FROM FURTHER ATTACKS.

SHORTLY AGAIN

...YOUR TRANSACTION IS COMPLETED. PLEASE TAKE YOUR CASH FROM THE Y-FRONT SLOT.

~ SNIFF SNIFF ~ HERE! THIS TEN POUND NOTE SMELLS!

AND LOOK ~ IT'S GOT A SKIDMARK ON IT.

IS THERE SOMETHING WRONG WITH FELIX'S PANTS?

THE PANTS MUST BE IN FINANCIAL DIFFICULTY!

APPARENTLY THE SKIDMARK HAS FALLEN AGAINST THE POUND!

QUICK, I MUST WITHDRAW ALL MY MONEY!

ME FIRST!

NO, ME!

ONE AT A TIME! YOU COULD DAMAGE THE NYLON INFRASTRUCTURE!

THAT'S TORN IT!

CLATTER

RT-T-T-P

THE BOTTOM HAS FALLEN OUT OF MY UNDERPANTS

THAT EVENING AT HOME

..FOLLOWING SCENES OF PANIC IN FULCHESTER HIGH STREET TODAY, THE GOVERNMENT STEPPED IN WITH AN EMERGENCY TAKEOVER OF FELIX'S UNDERPANTS..

TSK!

FELIX, FOR HEAVEN'S SAKE WILL YOU ASK THE BANK OF ENGLAND TO KEEP THE NOISE DOWN IN YOUR PANTS. I'M TRYING TO WATCH TELLY!

SORRY DAD.

LETTERBOCKS

Viz Comic
PO Box 656
North Shields
NE30 4XX

letters@viz.co.uk

Yonder Star Letter

WHAT A rip-off these "Tsars" the government keeps appointing are. They all look like grey-haired ex-assistant chief constables or polytechnic lecturers in boring suits. Not one of them wears one of those big furry Russian hats or has baggy silk trousers tucked into their boots, and none of them do that dance where they crouch down on their haunches and kick their legs out with their arms folded whilst shouting "Hai!". Come on, Mr Brown, you'll have to appoint some proper Tsars if you want my vote at the next election.

Umberto Bongo, Leeds

THESE people who go around saying that the best things in life are free clearly haven't read *The Metro*.

Christina Martin, London

FRUMPY middle-aged women. Save your energy by not lusting after Cliff Richard. I've worked backstage at his gigs and his cock is tiny.

N Nurse, e-mail

HOUSEWIVES. Wean your husbands onto raw eggs without them realising by removing the sand from your egg timer one grain at a time.

Tim, Brighton

CITY Link. Tell your customers that when the driver ticks "We'll try again the next day", he actually meant to tick the "Come and pick your package up from the depot" box. When your customer points out that the driver gave a specific time for the delivery, claim that your local branch "No longer re-delivers the next day for H-grade packages", whilst scribbling an 'H' on the package with a permanent marker when you think he can't see.

Gary, Eltham

JURY foremen. Add suspense to a verdict by saying "We the jury find the defendant..." and then leave a two minute pause before delivering the outcome whilst another jury member plays a low roll on a kettle drum.

Edna Spinosa, Newant

IN HIS public apology over the Sachsgate affair, Russell Brand said that all he's ever wanted to do was make people laugh. Okay, Russell, any time you're ready.

R Tanner, Hove

I WAS always taught at school that if a word had the letter 'Q' in it, it had to be followed by the letter 'U'. So how come Osama Bin Laden's terrorist group Al Qaida are allowed to get away with breaking this rule? They should be forced to spell their name properly - Quaida. Otherwise, in my opinion, these monsters have won.

Colonel Gowans-Whyte, Salisbury

THAT bird who reads the weather after the evening news only knows it's going to rain because she heard the bloke who reads the weather after the lunchtime news say it. Come on, love, do your own weather forcasting, eh? Cheats never beat.

Fat Al White, Wrenthorpe

I MUST say that I am enjoying the *X-Factor* much more than usual this year. I suspect this may be due to my having been out of the country whilst it's been on.

Gill Sansbold, Tring

I CAN understand all the fuss over Jeremy Clarkson's joke about lorry drivers killing prostitutes. I am a lorry driver myself, and I was deeply offended. I can assure Mr Clarkson that it's hitch-hikers we murder on a regular basis. The man should think before he opens his mouth in future.

Drayton Mannors, Torquay

ON A recent trip abroad, I noticed that my phrase book contained the sentence "Will you marry me?" Call me old fashioned, but surely no marriage that requires the use of a phrase book during the proposal is going to last.

Franklyn Gothic, Harpenden

IS TURKEY magnate Bernard Matthews dead, only we don't see him on his adverts anymore? You'd think that what with Christmas coming up and everything, he'd be trying to increase his profile a bit.

Arthur Turpin, Auchtermuchty

WITH reference to the above letter, I always used to get TV turkey farmer Bernard Matthews mixed up with TV dairy farmer Ted Moult, who shot himself, but who still appears on the Everest double glazing adverts.

Dr J L Seagull, Crystal Palace

I HOPE Bernard Matthews doesn't follow in the footsteps of Ted Moult and shoot himself. Although if he did, like Moult, we might start to see him on his adverts again, which would be nice.

A Chimneypot, Hades

I READ with dismay that the BBC is intending to re-make the classic children's TV series *Bagpuss*. Presumably, they'll spoil it by using fancy computer graphics, and completely destroy the appeal of the simple, charming original series with their trendy use of bad language, *Grand Theft Auto*-style extreme violence and explicit sex. Well, I for one have no desire to see a 3-D Professor Yaffle and Gabriel the Toad spit-roasting Madeline the ragdoll whilst Bagpuss masturbates, culminating in a mass bukkake cum-bath featuring the mice off the mouse organ. Why can't these people simply keep their filthy ideas to themselves and leave this innocent programme alone?

Mrs Seethe, Keele

A Hamper for your Tragedy

I BOUGHT a puppy for my 3-year-old daughter's birthday. However, when I got it home I discovered that it was blind and had no legs or ears. My daughter vowed to love it anyway, but the following morning it was dead. My daughter was so upset that she shot herself.

Destiny Plasterboard, Leeds

* Mrs Plasterboard's fantastically tragic tale of heartbreak means that she'll be celebrating Christmas this year with a £500 luxury Christmas hamper! Belgian chocolates, champagne truffles, liqueur mince pies and a selection of fine cheeses are all included.

The Funny Side of Marriage!

WHEN my husband started coming home in the early hours with lipstick on his collar, I was worried that he was having an affair. How foolish I felt when I confronted him with my suspicions and he explained that he had got a job on the night shift in a factory where they test shirt collars for resistance to lipstick!

Mrs Nora Cretis, Jarrow

5 YEARS after we got married, my wife and I applied for passports. When I looked at her form, she had a completely different name from the one I was expecting - it was the name of someone I'd never heard of. After talking about it, we realised that there must have been a mix-up at the registry office on our wedding day, and somebody else must have taken my wife home. Over the time we had been together, I had grown quite fond of the woman I had been living with, but I nevertheless decided to trace my actual wife. When I found her and told her what had happened, she was stunned. However, she was happy with the man who had inadvertently taken her home, and so we decided to leave things as they were. That was over 30 years ago, and the four of us still meet up for drinks every Christmas!

Derek Bowels, Penrith

THE VIZ PHONE-IN

Celebrity Kerry Katona is seldom off our screens. Whether she's stuffing her face with budget frozen food, or stuffing her face with essential medication, she's always there. But the question is why? Celebrity boffins are baffled as to the source of her fame, so we're having a vote to decide once and for all. Dial in and vote now! What do YOU think Kerry Katona is famous for?

DON'T KNOW 01811 8055
NOT SURE 018118056

Or text **KERRY** to 80812 followed by the words **DON'T KNOW** or **NOT SURE**

Last week we asked you how tall TV presenter Dermot O'Leary was. Here's how your votes stacked up: 4" 9" 68% • 5' 11" 29% • Don't know 3%

IS IT me, or does Eamonn Holmes look more and more like the Honey Monster every day?

Naich, Cambridge

DOES anyone else think, like me, think that if a zombie invasion were to break out, it would be quickly and efficiently taken care of by the authorities? In my opinion, films such as Night of the Living Dead and Zombie Flesheaters 2 are just irresponsible scaremongering.

Andy Woolfoot, Cirencester

I WAS worried that the government's planned ID card programme was the start of a slippery slope towards a totalitarian state where the authorities would keep tabs on us all 24 hours a day. However, when I saw the Home Office's logo for the scheme, my fears of this Orwellian nightmare were immediately laid to rest.

Morris Allenkey, Redruth

You cant go out like that you look like a tart

AW dad

Frankie "Ironfist" London
the Viz Heavyweight Consumer Champion

FIGHTING FOR YOUR CONSUMER RIGHTS

Dear Frankie,

I RECENTLY bought a new digital camera to take pictures at my daughter's wedding. I paid £48.99 at my local camera shop, Snappy Days in Hartlepool. However, when I got it home I discovered that the small door over the memory card slot was broken. I took the camera back but the assistant refused to give me a refund, saying that I must have broken it myself.

Ralph Titball, Cleveland

Frankie Writes:

I went round to see Mr Philips, the manager of Happy Snaps on Appleton Street, Hartlepool. I started off with a quick left to the jaw, which knocked out a couple of his teeth. That sent him off balance a bit, so I followed it up with a couple of swift jabs to the kidneys. He staggered backwards and fell awkwardly over a chair, so straight away I moved in with my boot. I stood on his throat and gave him few quality toe-enders in the ribs. He wasn't getting up after that, but I gave his face the millimetre tread for good measure.

SORTED!

Dear Frankie,

I SENT off for a new hosepipe reel from Ajax Garden Products of Redditch. They debited £24.50 from my card within a day, but 4 weeks later I had still to receive my hose. I called to complain, and was told that the company was having stock problems and my payment would be refunded. However, when I checked my bank statement later that month I saw that they had in fact taken a second payment of £24.50 off my card.

Percy Grainger, Ossett

Frankie Writes:

I found out where Brian Jookman, the owner of Ajax Garden Products, lives from records at Companies House, and I paid him a visit late one Saturday night. When he answered the door, I kneed him in the groin. Then I got him in an arm lock and, whilst wearing a duster, gave it to him again and again in the mush. He tried to fight back, hooking his foot round the front of my leg to get me off balance, but I'm no mug and I took the skin off his shins with my heel. The noise brought his wife and kids down stairs, but I told them to keep out of it, this was between me and him. I back-heeled him in the knee and I heard it pop. He screamed and went down like a sack of spuds. Before I left, I gave his face the millimetre tread for good measure.

SORTED!

Dear Frankie,

THE OTHER day I received a bill from Scottish Gas for £65.22. I'm a pensioner and I live on my own in a one bedroom bungalow and I don't use that much gas. They've estimated the bill this time as I was out when they came to read the meter, but I think it's a bit high as I usually pay around £55 per quarter.

Morag McGrew, Auchtermuchty

Frankie Writes:

I went round to Scottish Gas headquarters in Edinburgh, grabbed hold of the first bloke I saw and shoved him up against the wall. His glasses came off and I dragged him by his tie across the office and slammed his face into a desk. Another geezer came across playing the hero and tried to pull me off, but a quick elbow in the old solar plexus sent him sprawling into the water cooler. By this time security had come in and two of them tried to get me on the deck, but I was pumped up on test and they didn't stand a chance. I bit one of them on the bridge of the nose and put my thumb into the other one's eye. Four blokes were now down and out of action, but I gave all their faces the millimetre tread for good measure.

SORTED!

ARE YOU IN DISPUTE WITH A COMPANY?
WRITE TO: Frankie "Ironfist" London, Viz Heavyweight Consumer Champion, PO Box 656, North Shields NE30 4XX

THE YOUNG HOOLIGANS SNATCHED A STARTLED JADE GOODY FROM HER THERAPY TREE

I GOT HER! LET'S GO!

SHRIEKING WITH PANIC THE BIG BROTHER STAR BEGAN TO THRASH AROUND WILDLY

OOO-OOO-OOH! AH! AH! AH!

LOOK OUT! I CAN'T SEE WHERE WE'RE GOING!

CRASH! JADE LEAPT FROM THE CAREERING MOTORBIKE JUST BEFORE IT SMASHED HEADLONG INTO A TREE

AS THE TEENAGERS LAY UNCONSCIOUS, PETROL SEEPED FROM THE BIKE'S CRACKED FUEL TANK

NEARBY

FIRST AID

THERE ~ AMY WINEHOUSE WILL SOON BE FIGHTING FIT AGAIN.

SUDDENLY

DAD! HERE COMES JADE GOODY!

OOH! OOH!

AH! AH!

MY WORD! SHE'S LOOKING MORE AGITATED THAN USUAL

JADE BEGAN PERFORMING BACKFLIPS AND JABBERING URGENTLY

I-I THINK SHE WANTS TO SHOW US SOMETHING

YEEK! YEEK!

COME ON ~ LET'S FOLLOW HER

AND SHORTLY

IT'S THOSE TWO NE'ER-DO-WELLS ~ THEY'VE HAD AN ACCIDENT!

YES ~ AND THAT BIKE IS LIABLE TO EXPLODE AT ANY MOMENT

WE MUST QUICKLY GET THEM TO SAFETY ~ BUT THEY'LL BE TOO HEAVY FOR THE THREE OF US TO CARRY

DON'T WORRY COLIN ~ I'LL SUMMON SOME HELP

JIM UTTERED A STRANGE CRY WHICH ECHOED THROUGH THE PRIORY CLINIC GROUNDS

AAIEE - AYIAA - AAYIAAA!

MOMENTS LATER ERIC CLAPTON LUMBERED OUT OF THE BUSHES

QUICKLY KIDS, GRAB SOME OF THOSE CREEPERS AND MAKE THEM INTO A HARNESS

THE VETERAN EX-COCAINE ADDICT SOON PULLED THE UNCONSCIOUS RUFFIANS TO SAFETY

FORWARD, ERIC CLAPTON! UNGAWA!

THEY WERE NOT A MOMENT TOO SOON, AS THE MOTORBIKE EXPLODED IN A FIREBALL

KABOOM!

PHEW! WE WERE NOT A MOMENT TOO SOON!

LATER

I SAID EARLIER THAT CELEBRITIES OWE THEIR SUCCESS AND GLAMOROUS LIFESTYLES TO US, THE GENERAL PUBLIC

AND YET IRONICALLY, AFTER WHAT HAPPENED TODAY, IT IS WE WHO OWE OUR LIVES TO THESE CELEBRITIES

THE TWO TEENAGERS LEARNT THEIR LESSON, AND FROM THAT DAY ON THEY SMARTENED THEMSELVES UP, GOT A PROPER HAIRCUT AND LEARNT A BIT OF BLOODY RESPECT

KATE MOSS ENCLOSURE

OFTEN TIMES THEY WOULD CALL IN AT THE PRIORY CLINIC TO VISIT JIM AND THE CHILDREN, AND TO HELP OUT WITH THE CELEBRITIES' REHABILITATION DISPLAYS.

MERRY CRUN[...]

IT'S the time of year when we all push the boat out. Extravagance, excess and expense all help put the 'X' into Christmas every year. But 2008 is set to be very different. The global banking crisis has sent us all into a financial meltdown, and with no money to spend, Santa is going to have to tighten his belt and re-invent the festive season.

Out go expensive presents, tables groaning with yuletide goodies and halls decked with extravagant decorations. But it's not all doom and gloom, because successful *Shoestring* actor Trevor "Christmas" Eve has launched a brand new website that he hopes will give cash-strapped Brits a yule to remember at a tiny fraction of the usual cost.

"Filming two series of my detective show Shoestring back in the seventies was tiring work. That's why I decided to take two decades off before doing *Waking the Dead*," he told us. "After twenty penniless Christmasses, I'm something of an expert when it comes to making ends meet during the festive season."

As the recession starts to bite, Eve has decided now is the perfect time to pass some of his hard-worn tips to the hard-up public. His site **www.christmasonashoestring.co.uk** is packed with hints, tips and advice to help us enjoy a traditional family Christmas without breaking the bank. And here, we take a look at *Trevor's Top Twelve Christmas Tips.*

> ## "I'm something of an expert when it comes to making ends meet during the festive season!"
>
> ~ Trevor Shoestring

CHRISTMAS EVE: Trevor Shoestring launches his money-saving website yesterday. (*Picture courtesy of Batley & Spen Telegraph & Argus*)

THE TWELVE WA[...]

On the first way of Christmas, my Shoestring save to me ten pounds and fifty-five pee...

"A TREE is the centrepiece of our Christmas decorations, but it can easily cost £21.10 or more. Not only that, half the time we're not even looking at it because we're fast asleep in bed! Save 50% of the cost of yours by organising a tree-sharing scheme with a neighbour who works on a night shift. Enjoy the tree in your living room all day, then simply pop it round next door just before you go to bed and he gets back from work. He can return it to you the next morning, when you're getting up and he's just off to bed for a well-earned kip!"

On the second way of Christmas, my Shoestring save to me two thirty-one...

"ENERGY has quadrupled in price in the last twelve months. You only have to look at your electricity bills to see how much it costs to light your home through the dark winter months. Add that set of twinkling fairy lights on your tree and the expense gets even higher. This year, turn them off every time you leave the room. For greater economy, sit with the switch on your lap and turn your fairy lights off every time you glance away from the tree. And when you blink. You'll be amazed how much you save!"

On the seventh way of Christmas, my Shoestring save to me seven pounds and sixteen...

"WE ALL love the sound of carol singers, wassailing from door to door as the winter nights draw in. But these days the cost of heating our houses is horrendous, and every time we open the front door to carol singers, that precious heat escapes. It's literally like throwing pound notes into the street. So, when they turn up on your step this year, keep the door tightly shut and listen to them by holding a glass up to it. Then, when they've finished, reward them in the traditional way - with a delicious, hot mince pie poked out through your letterbox."

On the eighth way of Christmas, my Shoestring save to me eight pence in gravy...

"EVERY Christmas day, the average British household throws away half a pint of gravy. It might not sound a lot, but over 12 years it adds up to nearly a pound's worth of the stuff put straight into the bin, so gravy is an area where economy is essential. Start by making your gravy with half your usual amount of granules. If the resulting stock is too thin, which it will be, you can thicken it up using a tablespoon of wallpaper paste. And by simply placing a brick into your gravy boat, you can cut waste even further. These same techniques can also be used to save on custard, cream and brandy sauce."

YS OF CHRISTMAS WITH *Trevor Shoestring*

On the third way of Christmas, my Shoestring save to me three pounds ten...

"CHRISTMAS dinner is a blowout that often costs us more than we can afford. This year, instead of stuffing that nobody eats anyway, pop your Christmas pudding inside the turkey. It will cook at the same time as the main course, meaning you can turn the oven off early, saving valuable gas. And the savings don't end there. Set your wife up as a Public Limited Company and the pound coin she puts in the pud will be tax exempt, meaning it only costs 60p in real terms."

On the fourth way of Christmas, my Shoestring save to me four forty-four...

"FOLLOWING the main course, the Christmas pudding is served, and there is no more festive spectacle than the moment it is doused with half a bottle of booze and set alight. But even the cheapest supermarket own brand brandy will set you back the best part of a £8.88, so why not use some other flammable liquid from under the sink? Paraffin, paint brush cleaner or metal polish will all go up a treat on top of your pud. And don't worry about spoiling the taste. Your pudding's already wrecked because you cooked it inside the turkey!"

On the fifth way of Christmas, my Shoestring save to me five who-ole quid...

"CHESTNUTS roasting on an open fire is as synonymous with Christmas as the holly & the ivy or mistletoe & wine. But at £5, the price of coal and logs means that open fires don't come cheap. Meanwhile, all the heat from the works in your television is simply going to waste. Take a tip from me and remove the back from your telly and roast your chestnuts on the red hot, glowing valves. They'll taste all the better for having been cooked using heat that would otherwise have simply evaporated into thin air."

On the sixth way of Christmas, my Shoestring save to me six pounds and fourpence...

"EVERYONE loves receiving presents. And whether it's a pair of socks, a bottle of Pagan Man aftershave or another pair of socks, eagerly tearing off the wrapping on Christmas morning is half the fun. Wrapping paper is expensive, but believe it or not, one sheet is all you need to wrap up the whole family's pressies! Use your single sheet to wrap your first present. Then, once that's been opened, use the same piece again to wrap up the next gift. Do the wrapping whilst hidden under a blanket to maintain the sense of surprise."

On the ninth way of Christmas, my Shoestring save to me nine pounds and forty...

"ASK ANY true blue Brit what the best part of Christmas is, and he's sure to say The Queen's Speech. We all look forward to Her Majesty's Christmas royal address and we wouldn't miss it for the world. But the cost of watching it on TV is not inconsiderable. So this year, why not watch the speech with the volume turned down and the subtitles on? After all, we all know what she sounds like. To make an even greater saving, try listening to the speech on the radio whilst looking at a five pound note or a stamp."

On the tenth way of Christmas, my Shoestring save to me ten pounds and fifteen...

"CRACKERS come in a variety of price ranges, but even the cheapest ones can set you back a pound each. If you have a large family sitting down to dinner, the cost soon adds up. But a single cracker can be made to serve the needs of the entire family. After your cracker has been pulled the first time, push the contents back in, tape it together again and pass it on to the next person. Each time it is pulled, get someone to slam a door to recreate the bang. Everyone takes a turn with the hat and reads the joke silently to themselves so as not to spoil it for the next puller."

On the eleventh way of Christmas, my Shoestring save to me eleven pence in batteries...

"I DON'T know about you, but I watch a lot of TV over the festive season. In fact, telly is as much a part of Christmas as turkeys, mulled wine and the baby Jesus. But broadcasters have an annoying habit of increasing the sound level during commercial breaks, and when this happens it's tempting to reach for the remote control and turn the volume down, only to turn it back up again when your show comes back on. Before you know it, your remote control batteries are flat. Why not wear a Sherlock Holmes-style deerstalker hat and pull the flaps down firmly over your ears during the ads?"

On the twelfth way of Christmas, my Shoestring save to me twelve hours of expense...

"EVEN IF you follow all my previous tips, Christmas is still an expensive time of year. But there is a way to have a dream Christmas on virtually nothing. On December 24th, simply make yourself a hot toddy of Horlicks, whisky and grated cheddar, drink it and go to bed. The whisky and Horlicks will knock you out like a light whilst the well-known dream inducing properties of cheese will ensure that your slumber is filled with visions of the perfect Christmas. Keep a flask by the bed in case you wake up before Boxing Day. My wife, her out of the Gold Blend adverts, calls this festive cocktail 'Trevor's Christmas Drink'!"

□ MY husband is a doctor and he always insists on repairing his own boots. Every time he sets to work, he chuckles to himself and says "Physician, heel thyself". I haven't the heart to tell him that the correct quotation is "Physician, heal thyself", meaning "cure".
Mrs J Bodkin Adams, Eastbourne

□ MY wife used to be a pantomime actress, but left the theatre to take up a post working in the septic haemorrhage department of the London Hospital for Tropical Diseases. She has to wear wellingtons at work because she spends so much time wading through mucupurulent discharges on the floor. She often jokes that whereas she used to be in Puss in Boots, these days she's in boots in pus!
George Corbett, London

□ WHAT a load of rubbish these so-called safety boots with steel toe-caps are. They certainly didn't prevent any injuries happening to the person who pushed in front of me in the taxi queue on Saturday night.
Big Jim, Byker

□ I thought my boyfriend would find it a turn-on if I he saw me in thigh-length boots, but it didn't work out like that. I went into the branch of Boot's the Chemist where he works, in the Shropshire town of Thighlength, to buy some tampons and pile ointment, and I have to say that it didn't do anything to spice up our relationship.
Renee Bradawl, Thighlength

□ AS a keen gardener, I usually end up with a lot of lefto- ver fruit stored in my shed over the Autumn. In the past this often got nibbled by mice, but then my wife suggested storing it in an old wellington. My wife and I are forever joking that, instead of a pair of boots, we've got a boot of pears! Unfortunately, after being left for several months festering inside one of my old rubber galoshes, the pears taste fucking disgusting.
Urquhart Ffitzsimmons, Surbiton

□ MY grandad bought a pair

These Boots are Made for WALKEN

Hi, I'm Christopher Walken out of *The Deerhunter*, and when I'm not appearing in over 100 films, including *The Deerhunter* and over 99 more, I love to read your fascinating letters about boots. Anyway, that's enough about me, let's see what's been in my "boot"-iful mailbag this week!

Britain's Brightest Boot Forum, edited by Christopher Walken out of The Deerhunter

of climbing boots during the War and do you know, they're still as good as new. That's because they didn't fit him so they're still in the box on top of his wardrobe.
Sidney Durbridge, Tadcaster

□ AFTER 40 years working for the same company, I recently got given the boot. But I wasn't upset, because it was a golden boot with a clock in it, presented to me by my boss - the chairman of Dr Marten Boots Ltd. However, I had to give it back when I was sacked a couple of days later for stealing a typewriter.
Bert Plywood, Northampton

□ AS AN evil scientist, I have just completed construction of a giant, invincible metal robot, equipped with Death-Ray laser eyes, which I intend to unleash upon every major city in the world, causing un- told havoc and destruction. Its feet are made out of steel in order to crush anyone foolish enough to stand in its way - and ironically they are made out of car boots, which I bought at a local scrapyard!
Professor Skull, Death Island

□ "IS there a doctor in the house?" asked the theatre manager, when an actor had collapsed on stage during a play I was attending. "Yes, there's two here," I replied, before making my way up onto the stage. Once there, I pointed to my boots and said, "My Dr Martens!" Unfortunately the actor died, which took a bit of the shine off my quip.
Jack Chisholm, Spermford

Only Jokin' 'bout Bootz!

Americans call their car boots "trunks". In the UK, that's what elephants wear at swimming baths!
Only Jokin'! ~ Chris

Only Jokin' 'bout Bootz!

Boots aren't just for feet. Cars have boots too - they're called tyres!
Only Jokin'! ~ Chris

Your Boot Jokes

Knock-knock!
Who's there?
The Duke.
The Duke Who?
The Duke of Wellington boots!
Mrs F Discharge, Dundee

Knock-knock!
Who's there?
Duke.
Duke Who?
Duke (W)Ellington! (boots, like the jazz band man).
Mrs F Discharge, Dundee

Q: What sort of boots does David Beckham wear?
A: *Football boots.*
Mrs J Motson, Goole

Q: Why was the boot condemned to be cast into a lake of fire for all eternity?
A: *Because, on the Day of Judgement, it failed to get down upon its knees before our Lord and Saviour Jesus Christ, confess its sins and beg Him to save its "sole" from damnation.*
Dr Stephen Green, Wales

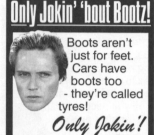

KIDS SAY THE FUNNIEST THINGS ABOUT Boots!

I am a Hell's Angel with size 14 feet, and I mentioned at home recently that I was on the lookout for a pair of large motorcycling boots. "There's a pair on the telly right now, Daddy," piped up my 5-year-old son. He was referring to the programme Two Fat Ladies, featuring Clarissa Dickson-Wright and Jennifer Patterson!
Dirtyarse, Tunbridge Wells

BOOT TEXTS

i jst trd n a dog sh1t! ne1 wnt 2 cln my bootz? lol - bootsie bill, leeds
Clean yr own boots :(only jokin! ;) shitty sal

HA HA NO THANX BILL - ENUFF BOOTZ OV MY OWN 2 CLEAN! BOOTMAN

no laffin matter. my uncle wos cleanin shit of his boots an got that disese wher he went blind. serious charlie

FUK YR SHITY BOOTS BILL>MY BOOTS IS CLEAN ASA WHISLE - VINCE BIRMINGHAM

u boot saddoes make me puke .shooes rool, tommy shoeman mcguire, belfast

FUCK U TOMMY SHOEMAN SHOES R 4 PEDOS - FARNHAM BOOT CREW

1 boot - 2 boots. 1 foot - 2 feet. WOTS ALL THAT ABOUT?! -Bamber

Only Jokin' 'bout Bootz!

Some people get very attached to their old boots. Paul McCartney even married one - Heather Mills!
Only Jokin'! ~ Chris

★★★ Only in America! ★★★

A PENNSYLVANIAN man recently made legal history when he successfully sued the estate of the Brothers Grimm for 'wilful misrepresentation'.

He claimed that whilst the Grimms' nursery rhyme stated that there was an old woman who lived in a shoe, the old woman had in fact lived in a boot, and that this inaccuracy had caused him such distress that he had grown up to be gay.

Mark Commode's BOOTS OF THE SILVER SCREEN

If you bought the DVD of the German film *Das Boot* expecting to watch a rollicking adventure about a boot, you'd be disappointed. That's because the film is actually just about a load of shouty Germans driving about in a U-boat. By a bizarre twist of fate, Will Hay's 1950s English film about boots, *Oh Mr Cobbler*, was released in Germany under the title *Das Submarine*.

It is a little known fact that Western actor John Wayne - real name Shirley Temple - had the smallest feet in Hollywood. In his most famous roles he was actually wearing Action Man cowboy boots - and even then 'The Duke' had to wear two pairs of hiking socks to stop them slipping off.

In the most famous scene from the 1924 silent classic *Hard Times*, Charlie Chaplin's tramp character is seen eating one of his own boots. Amazingly, it wasn't a prop but a real leather boot which was used. And Chaplin was such a perfectionist that he insisted that the sequence be reshot over and over again. In fact, he ended up eating an astonishing 37 boots before he was satisfied with the results!

IVAN JELICAL

HALL-ELUYAH!
HALLELUYAH! HALLELUYAH!

CHASE ME, IVAN!
NO, CHASE ME!

NEXT MORNING
FORGIVE ME MY TRESPASS, O LORD

ZZZZZ

SQUELCH
FRING

FOR SATAN HATH TEMPTED ME IN MY SLUMBERS, AND LO HATH I SPILLED MY SEED UPON THE STONEYCROFT

I HAVE PLACED MY IMMORTAL SOUL IN PERIL BY THIS ACT OF NOCTURNAL POLLUTION

KNOCK KNOCK

ST MARY'S VICARAGE

I MUST SEEK THE GUIDANCE OF THE VICAR IMMEDIATELY, FOR HE IS MY SHEPHERD, WHO WATCHETH HIS FLOCK BY NIGHT ALL SEATED ON THE GROUND.

YOU MUST NOT ALLOW THIS TO HAPPEN AGAIN, IVAN. DOES NOT THE BIBLE TELL US, "KEEP YOURSELF FROM THOSE DESIRES OF THE FLESH WHEN THE BODY IS YOUNG"?

2 TIMOTHY, CHAPTER TWO, VERSE 21

INDEED YES. JUST REPEAT TO YOURSELF WHEN YOU GO TO BED AT NIGHT: "TO THE CLEAN IN HEART, ALL THINGS ARE CLEAN."

TITUS CHAPTER ONE, VERSE 15

THAT NIGHT
"TO THE CLEAN IN HEART, ALL THINGS ARE CLEAN." TITUS 1:15. "TO THE CLEAN IN HEART, ALL THINGS ARE CLEAN". TITUS 1:15

YAWN!

"TO THE CLEAN IN HEART, ALL THINGS ARE..." ZZZZZ

CONGRATULATIONS, IVAN! YOU ARE CLEAN IN HEART, AND THEREFORE ALL THINGS ARE CLEAN!

ALL EXCEPT FOR THAT SPECK OF DIRT ON THE END OF YOUR TASSLE.

FLICK FLICK
FLICK FLICK

BUT DON'T WORRY! MY HOUSEKEEPER WILL SOON CLEAN IT OFF WITH A FEW VIGOROUS FLICKS OF HER FEATHER DUSTER!

NEXT MORNING
SOB! SOB! O MERCIFUL LORD IN HEAVEN... SOB! SOB!

SQUELCH

RAISE ME FROM MY ABYSS OF DESPAIR! SOB! SOB! SOB! SOB!

MAJOR MISUNDERSTANDING

GENTS

THERE'S NO POINT IN SUDDENLY LOOKING AT YOUR SHOES. I COULD SEE YOU EYEING ME UP BEFORE, YOU DIRTY BUGGER.

I'VE GOT EYES IN THE BACK OF MY HEAD, YOU SEE. THAT'S ARMY TRAINING FOR YOU. NOT THAT YOU'D KNOW ABOUT THAT.

YOUR SORT COULDN'T HACK IT IN THE ARMY. TAKES MORE THAN HALF-A-MAN TO DO A JOB LIKE THAT.

JANITOR

GOT NOTHING TO SAY FOR YOURSELF, EH? NO, I THOUGHT NOT.

YOU LOT MAKE ME SICK

CHAP CAN'T EVEN USE THE LAVATORY WITHOUT BEING SPIED ON BY SOME BLOODY PERVERT.

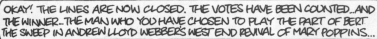